GREAT EVENTS
IN THE LIFE OF
MARK TWAIN

★5 *Starts his voyage to the*
Sandwich Islands, Hawaii, 1866

★6 *Marries Olivia Langdon*
in Elmira, N.Y., 1870

★8 *Starts worldwide lecture tour*
to pay his debts, 1895

★7 *Begins work on "The Adventures*
of Tom Sawyer," 1874

Tommy Johnson

THE STORY OF
Mark Twain

"STEEAMMM-BOAT *a-coming!*"

THE STORY OF
Mark Twain

By JOAN HOWARD

Illustrated by DONALD McKAY

ENID LAMONTE MEADOWCROFT
Supervising Editor

PUBLISHERS Grosset & Dunlap NEW YORK

For

DAVID AND HENRY NEWELL

*Who might have been friends
of Sam Clemens*

Contents

[*vii*]

CONTENTS

Illustrations

[*ix*]

THE STORY OF
Mark Twain

Sam was in the lead, with Will Bower right behind him

CHAPTER ONE

Sam Clemens Tries On
Some New Names

MISS MARY ANN NEWCOMB'S long, bony hand reached for the bell on her high desk.

"Recess, children!" she called.

That was something the teacher never had to say twice in spite of the racket in the room. There were twenty-two pupils of all ages in the tiny log schoolhouse. They made a lot of noise when they repeated their lessons aloud.

Sam Clemens was the first one on his feet in the rush for the door. Recess usually came only just in time to keep the nine-year-old redhead from doing something desperate. Sam thought it was a crying shame to waste the best hours of the day blabbing rubbish like Miss Mary Ann's old parrot. Especially a golden day like this one.

[3]

He glanced at his little brother. As usual, Henry was the only boy who had not stirred from his seat. Henry had only started school this term, but he already loved reading more than anything else. Even the First Reader held him fascinated.

Henry was handsome and smart, and he had winning ways. Sam was as fond of him as everybody else was. But he simply could not understand his brother. "The trouble is, Henry is just naturally a *good* boy," Sam guessed. "He can't help himself."

Nobody ever said that about Sam Clemens. Once outside the schoolroom, Sam forgot Henry. The yard was full of sure signs of springtime, shouting at him to escape while he could. Blossoms hanging heavy on the locust trees smelled sweet in the sun. Mud was drying off into dust, and Sam rubbed his bare feet hard along the ground. Except for the cut on his left big toe, he found they were toughening nicely.

Shooting marbles or playing three-cornered cat was not enough to celebrate such a day. Dodging between the girls' skipping ropes, Sam started a fast tag game.

[*4*]

"You're it!" he shouted, touching his best friend, Will Bowen. "Let's go fishing," he added in a lower voice. Then he raced away round the schoolhouse.

By the time Miss Mary Ann rang her bell to herd the children back into the schoolroom, four of her pupils had melted out of the yard. Sam was in the lead, of course, with Will Bowen right behind him.

Most days John Briggs would have come next. But John was home with measles, so Arch Fuqua took his place. Arch was a gangling boy who never said much, but he could crack his big toe with a snap that could be heard for thirty yards. Jimmy McDaniel was the last. The others let him come along because his father kept the candy store. Jimmy's pockets were usually stocked with licorice strings and horehound drops.

The boys reached the safe side of a clump of elderberry bushes.

"Hey, are you all playing hookey?" a voice asked from the bushes. "Can I go fishing with you?"

"Sure you can, Tom," Sam said. "I'd have asked you if I'd known where you were."

[5]

They never did know when they were going to run into Tom Blankenship—or where. He was supposed to live in a ramshackle cabin over Stringtown way. But his mother was dead and he didn't like his father, so he often stayed away for a spell. He ate whatever he could find or steal. Huckleberries, mostly, when they were in season. If it rained, he slept in a hogshead down at the tanyard.

Sam thought Tom was just about the luckiest boy in the world. Tom didn't have to go to school. He didn't even have to wash.

Of course, respectable folks were always telling their children to keep away from "that dirty boy." He was a disgrace to the town, they said. Sam Clemens thought that was unfair, when Tom was almost the only boy among them who had been born in Hannibal.

Hannibal, Missouri, was still too young for most of them to have been born there. Five years ago, it had been little more than a wood yard surrounded by a few cabins. Now it was a tidy white village where a thousand people lived and farmers came to market. The steamboat even stopped there regularly.

The five boys were as quiet as Indians in the

night till they reached the spot where their fishhooks and peeled hazel rods were stowed. They had picked this hideout for its central location in the middle of town.

It was a fine thicket of elderberry and hazel bushes. The bushes grew right where Bear Creek made a sharp elbow at the crossing of Main Street and Market. A heavy curtain of wild grapevine trailed over them. Here the boys were hidden from grown-up eyes, yet they could keep track of everything going on down at the levee. In case anything exciting happened, like a runaway or a fire, they could get to the scene in two minutes.

Now they baited their hooks and settled down to serious fishing. A quarter of an hour later, Will Bowen poked Sam.

"Wake up, Sam!" he said. "You've got a bite!"

The rod jerked in Sam Clemens' hand, and every freckle seemed to jump on his nose. He had not really been asleep, but he was a great boy for dreaming by day as well as by night.

A sudden whirl stirred the lazy water of Bear Creek. Sam's hook came up, with his bait worm gone.

[7]

"Aw, shucks," he muttered, "he got away—a whopper, too!"

"What was it—bullhead or catfish?" asked Tom.

" 'T wasn't any of your plain old fishes," Sam said in a soft drawl. The other boys called this drawl "Sam's long talk." It took him a little while to get words out, but mostly they were funny enough to be worth waiting for.

"What I had hooked there," he said now, "was a great big comet with a goldy yellow tail. A Halley's Comet."

"You're the biggest liar in Hannibal," Will declared.

Usually those would have been fighting words, for Sam's temper matched his fiery hair. From his friend Will Bowen, though, he took them with a grin.

"What *I* want to know is, what's a Halley's Comet?" Tom Blankenship asked.

"Well, a Halley's Comet is something like a shooting star," Sam explained. "Only a lot bigger. Its gold tail stretches clean across the sky."

"I'd mighty like to see that," Tom said.

"My mother told me it streaked over real

low the year I was born," Sam bragged. "Folks said it was a sign."

"Sign of what?" Tom's eyes were round with wonder.

His Negro friends on the levee and poor whites in shanty boats had told him a lot about signs and spells. Deathwatch beetles and howling dogs were always signs of bad luck. But a gold-tailed comet sure ought to bring good luck.

"Ma didn't say," Sam admitted. "Likely it's a sign I'm going to live till Halley's Comet comes back again. That ought to give me a nice long life. A hundred years maybe."

"You just think you're *some,*" Jimmy McDaniel jeered. He was worrying about playing hookey, and blaming Sam. "We'll get switched tomorrow," he predicted gloomily.

"Hush your big mouth," Sam told him. "You just ought to be glad our old schoolmarm don't board over at your house like she does at mine. She'll tell my folks right out at the supper table . . ."

"Then you'll catch it, won't you?" Will asked.

Sam nodded. He knew exactly how it would

[9]

be. Pa would *look* at him. Somehow, a look from Pa was worse than a whipping any day to Sam. He decided right then and there that he'd better just skip supper that night.

"How about a swim?" he asked.

"A *drown*, you mean." Jimmy thought his own words were so funny that he almost laughed a loose tooth right out of his head.

"The laugh's on you," Sam said cheerfully. "I can swim now as good as you can. It came easy after Tom gave me this certain-sure charm against cramp."

Tom blushed with pleasure when Sam showed off the ring of rattlesnake rattles wound round his ankle.

Swimming had not come naturally to Sam. He wasn't careful enough to stay in the shallows till he learned. So he had been hauled out of deep water again and again, practically dead.

"How many times *was* you drownded?" Arch Fuqua asked.

"Nine, by my count," Sam drawled. "That makes me cousin to the cat with nine lives."

"I s'pose you think that's special—being cousin to a cat," Jimmy teased.

[*10*]

"Are you trying to pick a fight?" Sam demanded. "I like cats."

Jimmy didn't really want trouble. He pulled a dusty licorice whip out of his pocket to share with the boys.

For a while the silence was only broken by chewing noises. Sam began to day-dream about the wonderful things he would do when he became a man. He was forever changing his mind, trying to decide whether to be sheriff or pirate or Indian scout when he grew up. But his favorite dream was the one he was dreaming now.

[*11*]

"Sawyer . . . Chalmers . . . Montgomery . . ." he mumbled through a wad of licorice.

"Huh? Is that a charm?" Tom asked hopefully.

"Nope," Sam said. "I'm trying on a new name for when I get to be captain of the *Big Missouri.*"

"You can't go changing your name," Jimmy argued.

"Can so," Sam drawled. "Easy as changing my clothes. Easier."

"Golly, I'd like to get me a short name," Tom Blankenship said. "So's I could learn to

write it in case anybody left me their money and I had to sign a paper to get it."

"Let's see . . ." Sam said thoughtfully. "How about Finn? It's easy—look!" Sam scratched the word FINN in the mud with his big toe.

Tom gazed at it respectfully. "I reckon I could learn that. Then what'll I do with Blankenship?"

"Blanken-*ship*," Sam repeated slowly. "Hey, that would make a fine name for a steamboat captain!"

"You can have it any time you want," Tom

said. "I'll give it to you free for nothing, because you're my friend."

Sam was pleased. Arch Fuqua gave his big toe an extra-loud crack. Then, all of a sudden, a distant yell brought the boys scrambling to their feet.

"STEEAMMM-BOAT a-coming!"

Every day the Negro drayman, John Hannicks, was first to spot a smudge of smoke way up past the point. His shout always brought the whole sleepy town on the run. The five boys lit out for the levee. They got there ahead of everybody else.

The *Big Missouri* gave a fine show as she came down the river. Her twin smokestacks streamed black clouds. Bells rang. Gaugecocks screamed. Her paddle boxes were newly gilded. Furnace doors were flung open, and the fires which had been freshly stocked with pitch pine reddened the whole mile-wide Mississippi River.

Tom and Will, Arch and Jimmy, all feasted their eyes on the boat. So did Sam Clemens. But in his mind he was not Sam Clemens any longer. He was the gallant Captain Blankenship up on the *Big Missouri's* hurricane deck.

He was shouting orders, and hearing his leadsman call the soundings.

"Mark twain!" yelled the leadsman.

That meant the water was two fathoms, or twelve feet, deep. The *Big Missouri* needed nine feet of river under her, so at "mark twain" she was in safe water.

When the steamboat churned on downstream, Will and Arch and Jimmy went home to their suppers. Tom Blankenship toted a traveler's carpetbag to Old Man Coleman's tavern. But Sam Clemens went on standing on the levee till the night settled down all round him.

"Mark Twain!" he said aloud to himself. "I think *that* would make a fine name for somebody."

CHAPTER TWO

Sam Clemens Gets into a Fight

SAM CLEMENS kicked a rock down the middle of the dusty Stringtown road. He ought to have been happy as a wood pigeon because he didn't have to waste this fine day in school.

"Even getting out of school isn't much fun all by yourself, though," he said out loud.

Sam had been clear out to Holliday's Hill without finding Tom Blankenship. Arch Fuqua had been dragged off to visit his starchiest aunt. Will Bowen's mother wouldn't let her boy out of the house.

"Just because his eyes are runny and he's got a few measly little red spots," Sam muttered in disgust.

Life had begun to go wrong for Sam soon

[*16*]

after the *Big Missouri* had gone on downriver. Skipping supper had seemed a good idea at the time. He had not been at the table when Miss Mary Ann told his family that he had played hookey. But he heard all about it.

He heard about it from his mother when she greeted him with a sharp thump on the head from her thimble. And from his sister Pamela, who thought, because she was nearly seventeen years old, she could tell her brothers how to behave. Then Henry told Sam exactly what everybody had been saying about him.

Only Pa did not say a single word. But he gave Sam a look that sent him up to bed feeling very low in his mind and very hollow in his middle. Pa's looks were worse, Sam decided, when a boy hadn't had any supper to fill up the hollow in his stomach.

The hungry hollow had kept Sam awake a long time. When he did drop off to sleep, he went bang into one of his bad nightmares. Sam often had dreams that made him shout and walk around all over the place without waking up. This one roused Henry, who shared the bumpy attic bed with Sam. Henry was scared and yelled for Ma. Altogether, the Clemens household had not had a restful night.

Things had looked brighter in the morning for a while, even with Miss Mary Ann at the breakfast table.

"I suppose you know, Sam," Miss Mary Ann said, "that there is no school today."

Sam was so surprised he choked on his cornmeal mush.

"Well, I *did* write a notice about it on the blackboard during recess yesterday," Miss Mary Ann had continued pointedly. "So many children are down with measles, we've decided to keep school closed until the epidemic is over."

Everything ought to have been wonderful after that. Yet here Sam was, mooching along past the haunted cabin on the Stringtown road. He was free as a bird, and so lonesome he would have welcomed Jimmy McDaniel even with empty pockets.

But he had not reached the point where he was glad to see Henry Beebe.

Henry had been Sam's pet enemy from the day the Beebe family arrived in Hannibal. Henry was rich and stuck up about his fine clothes. Henry had real brass artillery when every other boy had to use old spools for cannon in battle games. Henry had the only painted store sled, bought in St. Louis, that had ever been seen in Hannibal.

It was all very provoking to a redhead like Sam. But so far he had managed to keep his hands off Henry Beebe. That was just as well, because Henry was a year and a half older than Sam and about five sizes bigger.

Now here was Henry Beebe, peeking out at Sam from the haunted cabin. Sam wondered what Henry was up to in there. No good, he'd be bound. It made him mad just to think about Henry making himself at home in that place. Sam didn't dare to set a toe inside the door.

The ramshackle cabin had a sinister look about it. It sat, dirty and windowless, way back among tall cottonwood trees. Sam did not remember the old woman who had died there. But folks said she was a witch so ancient that she remembered Moses. Tom Blankenship had told Sam spine-chilling stories about her ghost coming to haunt the old cabin. He always wanted to get past the place as fast as he could without running.

[19]

Now a piercing whistle stopped him in his tracks.

"Hey, Skinny Carrot!" yelled Henry Beebe. "I bet you can't guess what I've got in here."

"Don't know, and don't care," Sam said defiantly, but not quite truthfully. He *was* curious.

Henry Beebe thrust one big hand through the wide crack where the door hung off its top hinge. The hand was squeezing too hard on something very tiny and furry.

"I hear tell you like cats," Henry jeered at Sam. "Do you want to come and watch me butcher this one?"

Sam felt sick. "You can't *do* that!"

"Sure I can. I've fixed me up a slaughterhouse, and I'll kill kittens exactly the way they kill pigs."

"You can't!" Sam shouted furiously. "I'll . . . I'll. . . ."

"You'll do what?" Henry asked with a grin. "No little runt like you can stop me." He stepped back into the dim room, taking the kitten with him.

Sam forgot that he was scared of the haunted cabin. He forgot all about Henry Beebe's size and reach. He rushed in and tore the kitten out of Henry's fingers. Henry was too astonished to stop him.

Henry's surprise did not last long. "No, you don't," he said, advancing with swinging arms.

Sam dodged the first blow only because he had stooped over. He was setting the baby kitten in a heap of old rags so he could use both hands.

It did not seem to Sam that he dodged a single swing after that one. He took two punches on his left ear that made it ring. He took one punch right in the eye, and three punches square in the mouth. But every time, he came back for more, butting with his red head when his shorter arms didn't reach Henry.

Sam Clemens never did know afterward how he did it. But somehow he got the big boy

down on the dirt floor. He was kneeling on the squirming Henry. His two hands had a firm grasp on Henry's black hair, and he was rubbing Henry's fat face in the earth with a joy he had never known before.

"That'll—teach you—" he panted, "to hurt —cats."

CHAPTER THREE

Mrs. Clemens Gets Another Cat

S AM!" The voice was his mother's.

Sam did his best to become invisible as well as silent. He tiptoed across the bare room to the steep box stairway. If he could reach the attic, he'd be safe long enough to mop off some of the blood which was splattered over his face and clothes. He kept one scratched hand pressed against a small lump that stirred inside his shirt.

Luckily his brother Henry had not seen him come in. It was a funny thing about good boys, Sam thought. They never could keep still, even when talking would get somebody into trouble. But Henry Clemens was feeding the cats out on the back stoop. That would keep

him busy for quite a spell. There were nineteen cats—nineteen outside, anyway—all
mewing for their suppers and weaving round
Henry's legs.

Sam wondered if his mother would notice
if he came down to supper in his other shirt.
Since he only had one other shirt, which was
his Sunday-go-to-meeting best, he decided she
would. He reached the stairs.

"Sam, you march right back down here! I
want to see you."

Mrs. Clemens came in from the kitchen,
holding a woollen sock stretched over her
darning egg. "Come here, Sam!"

"Yes, Ma." Sam moved toward his mother,
keeping a safe distance from her threatening
thimble. It seemed to him that she wore that
thimble just to thump his head. Right now his
head felt too sore to take another rap.

"You've been fighting again!" Mrs. Clemens said.

"No'm," Sam drawled. "Not fighting exactly. I got tripped up."

Then Sam thought he could make a good
story a little better.

"It was this way, Ma. You know the old witch's cabin out on Stringtown road? Well, I happened to be walking by there, minding my own business, when this ghost crept up behind me. . . ."

"That will do, Sam!"

Sam backed hastily out of the thimble's reach. He smiled at his mother. She saw the bloody gap where a tooth had been. His right eye was turning black.

"I declare to goodness, Sam, I don't know

what to do with you," she said. "First off, you were so sickly I thought I'd never raise you. Then you went through that spell of getting yourself drowned. Now it's fighting. Why can't you be a good boy like your brother Henry?"

"No'm. Yes'm. I don't know."

"What's that you're hiding in your shirt?"

Sam sighed and pulled out the kitten. It was no bigger than his hand, black with white paws and a white bib. Its eyes were still a new-opened blue. Its fur was matted with Sam's blood. He set the tiny creature down on the puncheon floor. It wobbled two steps and fell over.

"Why, it's hurt!" Mrs. Clemens scooped it up gently.

"Yes'm. That's why I had to fight Henry Beebe." Sam broke off. It wouldn't do to tell a lady about that play slaughterhouse. Not any lady who loved cats as much as his mother did. His ma could never bear to see anything hurt, not even flies and spiders.

"Say, Ma, if you think I'm a mess—" he began.

"I do, Sam," his mother said. "Look at your

clothes. And I'll have to put a poultice on that eye."

Mrs. Clemens was a great believer in poultices. And hot ashes in a sock wrapped round sore throats. And big doses of castor oil, with or without molasses, depending on the seriousness of the sickness. Her remedies all scared Sam worse than her thimble.

"This eye doesn't hurt one teeny bit, Ma. Honest. Look, I can open it wide."

Sam tried hard and managed to get it open a crack. Under the swollen lid, it gleamed green as a cat's. Sam's blue-gray eyes always turned green when he was excited.

"You ought to see Henry Beebe!" he bragged. "I bet both his eyes are shut tight."

"I'm surprised at Henry Beebe being mean to a helpless animal. He's always so tidy and polite—a real model boy, I thought." Mrs. Clemens held the kitten snuggled under her chin where it was practicing a brand-new purr.

But now that she stopped to think about it, she really wasn't so surprised. Probably young Beebe was like his father. And Mrs. Clemens had no use for Mr. Beebe. He was a smart man, all right, but not a very honest one.

Six months earlier, Mr. Clemens had owned a store in Hannibal. Then Mr. Beebe had moved to town. Somehow he had managed to take over the store. And only last week he had demanded money he said the Clemenses owed him.

Mr. Clemens had to sell the parlor furniture to pay it, and that was why this room was bare. The only thing left in it was Pamela's old piano. That was left so she could earn a little money giving lessons to the neighbors' children.

"I wonder if Pa will let us keep this kitten," Sam said. "He thinks we're crazy to like cats so much."

"Right now your pa has other things on his mind," Mrs. Clemens answered. "I'll give it to Muff to nurse with her kittens, and he probably won't even notice."

Sam's spirits zoomed. They always did when he and his mother were together in any plot.

He laughed. "I've thought of a name for her," he said. "It's Minniecat."

"All right, but you watch out, Sam. That redheaded temper will land you in trouble yet, and serve you right."

"Yes'm," said Sam.

He stared hard at his mother's hair. Her curls were redder than his, with only a few threads of gray in them.

"I reckon I take after you," he said impudently. "Tell me about throwing rocks at the man who was beating his horse."

Sam's mother laughed. She liked to tell stories about her Kentucky girlhood.

"Now, Sam," she began, "you know that happened way back when I was nothing but a tomboy. . . ."

Sam loved these stories. He was annoyed

when a voice outside the window broke into this one. It was a piercing voice belonging to Sandy, the little Negro houseboy. Once the Clemenses had had several servants. Now Sandy was the only one left. And that was just because he had been hired by the year from a back-country farmer.

Sam liked Sandy. They had a lot of good times together when they went to the town pump or toted wood. And good mischief, too, very often. But little Sandy's voice was as high and persistent as a mosquito in the night. And very much louder, going on and on. . . .

"I'm going out and make Sandy quit that racket, Ma," Sam said.

"You'll do nothing of the kind!"

"But it's awful! You don't like it, do you, Ma?"

"Of course I don't like it," Mrs. Clemens said. "But think, son. Sandy has to work a long way from home. He never gets to see his mother, poor little thing. When he is singing, it's a sign he's not homesick. The noise drives me almost distracted sometimes, but I'm always listening for it. It would break my heart if Sandy should ever stop singing."

Sam felt a scratchy lump in his throat. "I never thought about that, Ma."

"I know, Sam. Just don't forget it now."

"I won't, Ma. I won't ever forget it."

Suddenly Mrs. Clemens realized that her husband would be home any minute, and supper was not even on the stove.

"Here, Sam, take Minniecat to Muff. I've got to fly. And wash that blood off. I don't know what your father is going to say about this fighting."

"Yes'm. No'm," Sam said. Pa wouldn't say much. He never did, to Sam. But he would *look* again.

Mrs. Clemens paused in the kitchen doorway. "Pray the Lord to make you a better boy, Sam."

"Yes'm." Sam's voice was doubtful.

"You believe in prayer, don't you, Sam?"

"Reckon I do, Ma. The other day Miss Mary Ann made us pray in school. I prayed for gingerbread. When I opened my eyes that German girl, Maggie Koeneman, had a big hunk of gingerbread from her father's bakery. I could reach it as easy as anything. And I got two big bites before she grabbed it back."

[*31*]

Mrs. Clemens sighed. "That isn't just what I meant, Sam."

"No'm," Sam agreed. "I reckon not. I tried praying the same thing next day, too. But it didn't work."

CHAPTER FOUR

Sam Clemens Asks for Measles

SEVEN since yesterday . . ."

As he came down the steep stairs, Sam saw two heads close together—Miss Mary Ann's old-maidish one, and his sister Pamela's, which was covered with soft russet curls. The loud whisper was Miss Mary Ann's, with all the s's hissing like a teakettle on the boil.

Pamela caught sight of him. Then Miss Mary Ann swung round to peer upward. Sam thought she was growing to look more like her old parrot every day.

"My sakes, do you have to come pussyfooting to scare the wits out of a body?" the schoolmarm asked crossly.

Sam Clemens had often been scolded for the racket he made. But this was the first time he had ever been accused of being too quiet. So he knew he had overheard something he was not supposed to. He thought about the words.

"Seven since yesterday . . ."

It must mean that seven more children had died. Every year Hannibal youngsters had measles, of course. But the town had never known such a deadly epidemic as this one.

"Will and John—are they . . . ?" Sam hardly dared ask.

"Stop fretting," Pamela told him. "John Briggs is practically well. And Will Bowen is doing all right."

Pamela tried to act as if nothing was the matter. But she sounded worried.

"You keep away from other children, Sam," she said. "Especially that Tom Blankenship. Goodness only knows what he picks up."

"There you go, Pammy, talking mean about Tom again," Sam protested. "He's just as good as anybody else."

"Oh, don't be silly," his sister said sharply. "Nobody's talking about Tom not being as good as anybody else. Henry and I had measles two years ago. That keeps us from catching them again. But you missed them. It's about the only sickness you ever did miss. So show some sense for once."

"Sam showing sense would make a nice change," Miss Mary Ann put in acidly. But she sounded worried, too.

"Anyhow, you just stay home today," Pamela told Sam.

But they couldn't keep Sam in, not without tying him down. Hannibal did not offer much fun, though. The streets were as bare of children at noon as they usually were at midnight.

Sam went hunting for Tom Blankenship in all Tom's favorite places. He was not in Mr. Robard's haymow. Not by the town pump. Not over at the sawmill, nor down at the tanyard. He was not on the levee.

"I bet he's round back of the Wildcat Store," Sam told himself. "Tom always checks through the stuff Mr. Selmes throws out, in case there's anything to eat in it."

Today Sam Clemens couldn't even win a bet from himself. Tom wasn't behind the Wildcat Store. And Sam didn't dare go right out to the Blankenship shanty. He was too scared of old man Blankenship.

So Sam was left with a long afternoon ahead,

and nothing to do in it but worry. He was glad
John Briggs was getting well. But he began to
imagine that Pamela had sounded peculiar
when she spoke of Will. Maybe she was hiding
the truth. Sam worried about Will for a spell.
Then for a while he worried about himself,
and whether he was going to catch measles.

"No two ways about it," he thought. "I've
got to know."

He went along to Will Bowen's house, and
slipped round to the back while Mrs. Bowen
was sweeping her front stoop. He shinnied up
the crabapple tree and over to the kitchen
roof. He crawled through Will's window,
pushing aside the blanket Mrs. Bowen had
pinned up to darken the room. Sam left it
hanging crooked, so the light fell on Will's
blotchy face.

"What in tunket are you doing here?" Will
was surprised.

"Visiting the sick and afflicted like the
preacher says, Will."

Sick as he was, Will had to laugh.

"Besides," Sam said, "I got tired waiting to
see was I going to catch measles. So I came to
catch yours and get it over with. I'll climb into

bed with you and we can talk for a while."

Sam got into the bed. They talked about pirates, but Sam found it hard to hold Will's interest with his "long talk" today. Sam grew very hot under the covers with his clothes on. He shut his eyes to rest them. And he fell asleep.

"Sam Clemens, are you asking for measles?" Mrs. Bowen's voice brought Sam into the middle of the room in one jump. "I'm going straight to your house and tell your mother what you've been up to. Now, get out of here."

Sam didn't stop to say good-by. He left the Bowen house in a hurry, but he didn't dare go home. For hours he hid out down at Bear Creek. He meant to stay there all night but the dew was terribly heavy. Wet and shivering, he left the creek and padded through the silent streets just before moonrise.

He headed for the dingy one-room office his father used when he was acting as Justice of the Peace. Sam knew the office window had a broken lock. He opened the window and climbed through.

It was pitch dark inside. But there wasn't much furniture to stumble over. Just a dry-goods box that Pa used for a desk, and three stools and a puncheon bench. Sam reached the bench without bumping anything. He stretched out on it, wishing the wood was padded like the old horsehair sofa they used to have at home till it was sold.

"But if this was horsehair, it'd be so slippery I'd slide clean off," Sam told himself out loud. His own voice sounded strange in the empty room. It startled him.

Somehow the dark room did not *feel* empty. Sam wondered why. Maybe it was because his father had been there. Even a room couldn't forget his pa in a hurry, Sam thought. He went on thinking about his father. How everybody was always so respectful, even after Mr. Clem-

[38]

ens lost the store to Mr. Beebe. People never talked down to him the way they did to other poor folks. And they let him go right on being Justice of the Peace.

It was fine to have a father who was such an important man. But Sam wished an important man did not have to be so stern at home. He had never once heard his father laugh. Of course, maybe that was partly because of the blinding headaches Pa was forever getting, and his bad cough.

Sam was growing sleepy when moonlight began drifting in the window. Drowsily he watched a patch of pale light creep slowly across the rough floor. Before long it touched a dark hump in the middle of the room. Sam leaned almost off the bench to make out what it was.

At first it looked like a pants leg with a shoe on the end. Sam told himself that was silly. The shaft of moonlight moved on across a heap of cloth. Who would dare leave a bundle of old rags in the office of the Justice of the Peace?

Thin white clouds had been blowing across the moon. Now suddenly it shone full and

A glare lit up the thing on the floor

clear. A glare lit up the thing on the floor. Sam saw a white, staring face, and the handle of a knife sticking up out of the clothes.

In a split second Sam was off the bench. His yell splintered the peace in the Justice's room. Then he was out of the window, taking the sash with him. He couldn't stop to get rid of it. So he kept on running with a part of the window frame clinging to his middle.

Suddenly, right smack on Wildcat Corner, he ran headlong into his father. Sam was scared into stony silence.

Mr. Clemens looked taller than ever in the night, and darker and thinner. Even his blue swallowtail coat was black as a crow. His eyes gleamed a little in the moonlight.

Sam wanted the earth to swallow him up. He couldn't speak. He couldn't breathe. And when he felt his father's arm round his shoulders, he could not believe it.

"What is it, son?" Pa's voice was the biggest surprise. It was not icy cold with anger, but warm and comforting.

"A g-ghost's l-l-lying down in your office!" Sam tried to keep his teeth from chattering. "W-with a knife stuck in it!"

"Why, that isn't a ghost," Mr. Clemens said. "A poor fellow was stabbed in a fight down on the levee. They brought his body to my office so we could hold an inquest on it to-morrow, to find out all the facts in the case."

Pa did not even ask Sam what he was doing at the office late at night. He just tidied him up a little, and got rid of bits of wood and splinters which were sticking to his clothes.

When father and son reached home, Mrs. Clemens met them at the door, holding a candle. Sam could see fire in her eyes when she looked at him. The thimble glittered on her finger.

Mrs. Clemens looked from Sam to his father, and back again at Sam. She had never seen them so friendly before. It would be a shame to spoil it.

"I've kept your supper hot," was all she said.

CHAPTER FIVE

Sam Clemens Gets What He Asked for

SAM'S head ached as he watched the old doctor put down his scuffed black satchel. He was wishing he hadn't visited Will on purpose to catch his measles.

For one thing, the spots had taken a long time to show up. By the time he broke out, practically everybody else in town was getting well.

Until this year, Hannibal folks had never called a doctor for anything as simple as measles. But the epidemic had changed that. Dr. Meredith was the hardest working man in Missouri. He was a gruff man with a deep bass voice. Sam liked him because he had once shipped before the mast of a whaling schooner.

"Here we go again!" the doctor boomed at Sam. "From what they tell me, you certainly asked for measles. But from the minute this epidemic broke out, I knew I'd be getting you back as my steadiest patient."

Up to a year ago, Sam had been a very steady patient. First with a long list of sicknesses, then with his drownings. But since last summer he had been growing tough and wiry.

Dr. Meredith chatted cheerfully all the time he was peering down Sam's throat and feeling his burning skin and looking at his spots. But Sam managed to hear what the doctor said to Mrs. Clemens when he was leaving.

[45]

"He's taking this hard—the way he does everything. I only hope it isn't one of these cases of black measles."

Black measles scared Sam worse than red ones, though he knew nothing about them. He was still scared that night when the family went to bed. It was lonesome in the attic, just lying there looking out at the stars. He wished Ma hadn't made Henry sleep on a quilt down in the empty parlor.

Sam's head hurt. So did his throat. He began listening for night noises. He heard a sort of clicking in the wall and decided it was a deathwatch beetle. A long way off, a dog howled. Sam was ready to bet that dog was in the graveyard. Tom had told him that a howling dog in a cemetery was the worst sign of all.

For a second, he hoped that the next noise would be Tom himself under the window. When Tom wanted Sam to come out at night he used to mee-yow down there like a cat. Then Sam would mee-yow back and sneak out over the woodshed roof.

But tonight there was no mee-yow at all. Only an old owl some place hoo-hooing to another owl. Sam shivered.

[*46*]

"I'll go get Minniecat," he said. "She'll be company."

Sam tiptoed down to the kitchen, missing the creaky step. He lit a stub of candle and held it up to the looking glass over the washstand. His spots didn't look so black to him.

He pulled up his nightshirt to study the spots on his stomach. "Black measles," Doc had said. These weren't black. They were not even red like Will's; just sort of purple, about like huckleberries. Sam felt cheated because they weren't coal black. "If I've got black measles," he told himself, "I'm going to *have* black measles. Blackest anybody ever saw."

He rubbed his fingers inside the sooty fireplace and touched up the spots in front. He smeared the rest of the soot round his back, hoping it would match.

By that time he was so hot and dizzy he forgot all about Minniecat. He crawled back up to bed.

Next morning Mrs. Clemens' shriek roused her household. Before they could ask what was the matter, she was flying down the road with her checkered apron flapping in the wind. In no time at all, she was running home again

[*47*]

and Dr. Meredith puffed along behind her. In not much more time, the doctor was standing beside Sam's bed.

Sam kept his eyes shut when Dr. Meredith pulled back the covers and pulled up his nightshirt. He tried a feeble groan. The doctor's snort nearly blew him out of bed. Then he felt himself being scrubbed hard with a wet washrag.

"He told me it was black measles, Doctor," Mrs. Clemens said, sounding very anxious.

The doctor snorted again. "You ought to know better than to believe *anything* this boy says, ma'am. He couldn't behave himself if he was on his deathbed."

But when Sam was sick, his mother always stuck up for him. "Why, my Sam is a perfect well of truth," she declared. "It's only that you can't bring it all up in one bucket."

For the next few days Sam was out of his head from fever a good part of the time. He would come to and fight a little bit when socks of hot ashes were laid against his stomach. He shuddered when they wrapped him in icy wet sheets. For a couple of minutes he was right lively when he had to swallow castor oil.

Whenever he opened his eyes he saw a lot of folks around his bed. That pleased Sam. It showed proper feeling. His mother never left him. Pamela was there most of the time. Pa sat stiff and silent. Henry snuffled. Miss Mary Ann went on blowing her nose. There was a long mee-yow under his window. Nobody else paid any attention, but Sam knew Tom Blankenship was letting him know he was there.

Even Sam's big brother Orion came home from St. Louis where he was learning to be a printer. Sam wanted to ask Orion if Pa had sent for him. But somehow he could not make his voice come out, except in a croak like a bullfrog.

Once when Sam opened his eyes, he felt pretty mad. Henry had dropped off to sleep and Miss Mary Ann was nodding. Sam wanted to tell them it was no way to behave, with him almost dying.

Then Sandy sneaked into the room. And he balked like a mule when Mrs. Clemens tried to put him out because he'd never had measles. Finally she had to give up and let him stay.

[49]

Every day until Sam was on the mend,
Sandy sat in the corner. He sobbed and

howled. Sam felt that at last he had a proper
mourner. This time he did not mind the
racket the little Negro boy made. He didn't
want it to stop.

CHAPTER SIX

The Glorious Fourth of July

H IS first day out after measles, Sam met his
friends moseying along the riverbank. They
weren't doing anything in particular—just
whistling back at a couple of blackbirds, and
watching a log raft drift down past Glasscock's
Island.

"Hey, everybody thought you were a
goner," John Briggs said.

He and Will Bowen and Tom Blankenship
all inspected Sam. He looked pretty much as
usual, except a mite peaked. They had
thought that his coming so close to dying
would show on him.

"I 'most *was* a goner," Sam said proudly.
"But I got to thinking I might miss something
if I died. So then I didn't."

[*51*]

John Briggs was proud of himself, too. "This is the only time I ever got the jump on you, Sam. I was first to catch measles in Hannibal this year. And you were last."

"Last but one," Sam corrected him. "Our Sandy took them from me. He's still sick. Did you get them, Tom?"

Tom shook his head. Suddenly he changed the subject.

"What's a Revolutionary War hero?" he asked.

Sam looked at him in astonishment.

"Heck, everybody knows *that!*" he exclaimed.

Then he remembered that Tom hadn't ever been to school. So Sam explained to him about the war the Americans had fought with the British because they didn't want to be ruled by England any longer. He told Tom about George Washington and the Declaration of Independence. And about the Battle of Bunker Hill, and Valley Forge.

"The Americans fought those redcoats till they licked them good and proper," Sam went on. "And every soldier who fought in that war on our side was a Revolutionary War hero.

Why did you want to know about them?"

"Pete Smith that drives the stage said one of them heroes was living on a little farm only 'bout eight miles out," Tom replied, scratching a mosquito bite on his leg. "He said they was going to have him in the Fourth of July parade. But, shucks, I reckon Pete was just funning. A hero like that'd be a thousand years old by now."

"He wouldn't have to be," Will said. Will was good at arithmetic. "Look, you take 1776 from this here year which is 1844 . . ."

"*I* don't take it," Sam said quickly. "You do it."

So Will did the sum with a twig in soft riverbank mud. After a couple of tries, the answer came out sixty-eight.

"It's sixty-eight years since this fellow— this hero, I mean—joined up with George Washington to fight the redcoats," Will declared. "Now, say he was fourteen years old at the time. That'd make him—uh—eighty-two now."

"I wonder if a soldier eighty-two years old can still march in a parade," John Briggs said.

"A big hero like that ought to get to ride,"

was Tom's opinion. "He ought to sit up in a fine carriage like that fancy new one of Judge Draper's."

The boys soon found out that was precisely what was going to happen. Judge Draper was Hannibal's wealthiest citizen. He had offered his brand-new carriage for the use of the great Revolutionary War hero.

Soon everybody in town was talking about the hero. Folks wondered how he could have been living so close to Hannibal without their knowing it all these years. They were determined to make up for past neglect.

The town boiled with preparations for this Fourth of July. The stores and blacksmith shop and school were draped in red, white, and blue bunting. Some of the houses were decorated that way, too. And the window boxes of the rest were filled with geraniums as red as exploding fireworks.

On the afternoon of the third of July, Sam and his friends waited on the levee for the packet boat. It was bringing a real brass band from St. Louis. The bandsmen stood on the upper deck, with their brass instruments and gold-braided uniforms shining in the sun.

They looked so fine, Sam wondered if maybe he wouldn't become a bass drummer.

Sam had a hard time getting to sleep that night. Twice he climbed out on the woodshed roof to make sure the sky wasn't clouding over for rain. By sunrise, he was out on the street, munching on some dried apples and a piece of cold cornbread.

Outside the livery stable, he met Tom and Will. All three of them watched a light buggy set out to pick up the hero of the day.

"I thought he was all set to ride in Judge Draper's carriage," Tom said.

"So he is, for the parade," Sam said. "But they wouldn't want that fancy rig getting all dusty ahead of time."

The hours passed as slowly as snails crossing a road. But at last the buggy came back. The hero looked like any other very old farmer coming to market.

Tom was disappointed. "Where's his uniform? Why ain't he dressed up?" he asked.

"For the same reason they didn't send the carriage, of course," said John Briggs, stepping up to join the other boys. "So's he wouldn't get all dirty before he got to town."

[55]

"Look," Sam said, "there's Mr. Selmes helping him out of the buggy. Golly, he *is* old."

The guest of honor climbed down stiffly. He was holding onto a bundle done up in a blue spotted kerchief half as big as a table-cloth. Mr. Selmes led him into the Wildcat Store to change his clothes.

The boys went across to the Wildcat Store's front door to wait for the hero. They found they had picked the best spot in town for watching everything that went on.

First Judge Draper's coachman drove up with a fine flourish. He was wearing a red, white, and blue cockade in his hat to match the fancy big rosettes on the carriage wheels. Then the parade began to assemble round the carriage.

Will Bowen's father, who was the town marshal, was up in front to lead it. Behind him stood the brass band from St. Louis. Next the red-shirted Liberty Boys Volunteer Firemen rattled their ladders and buckets as they pulled up their handcart which was all draped in bunting.

Half a dozen trappers in coonskin caps, and

seven Indians in feathered war bonnets had been rounded up for the occasion. The children in the Old Ship of Zion Sunday School brought up the rear.

John Briggs had his ear against the store door, listening.

"Shhh! Get ready—he's coming!" John called.

Judge Draper, the blacksmith, and Mr. Clemens were the Reception Committee. They stepped forward to greet the Revolutionary War hero.

"Don't you get in the way now, Sam," Mr. Clemens said.

"I won't, Pa," Sam said. But he forgot his promise almost at once, for the door opened.

The hero stepped out, blinking a little in the sunshine.

"My, that's a right purty red coat!" Tom Blankenship's voice rose clear in the expectant hush.

"Redcoat?" repeated Judge Draper in a dazed tone.

"*Redcoat!*" exclaimed the blacksmith in a voice like a bellow.

"What's the matter?" Tom asked. "Hey,

Sam, why don't your pa begin his speechi-
fying?"

"Didn't I tell you the redcoats were our
enemies?" Sam exclaimed. "What's a redcoat
doing at a Fourth of July parade?"

Mr. Clemens found his voice at last.

"Sir, you have tricked us!" he roared furiously. "You are an imposter! *Get out!*"

The drum major could not see what was going on in front of the store. He thought Mr.
Clemens had shouted an order to strike up the
band. So he twirled his long baton.

The band started to play at the front end of

the procession. Way in the rear, the children in the Old Ship of Zion Sunday School began to sing the words as loudly as they could.

"Hail, Columbia! Happy Land!
  Hail, ye heroes! Heaven-born band!
  Who fought and bled in freedom's cause . . ."

It took the combined roars of the Reception Committee and the Liberty Boys Volunteer Firemen to get them stopped.

The old man shrank down into his ancient uniform like a turtle pulling in its head. He looked puzzled by all the shouting and confusion.

"Reckon there's been a mistake," he muttered. "First off they ask me to come. Now it seems they don't want me."

He did not go back into the store for his everyday clothes. He just started trudging off up the road. Nobody thought of offering him a ride back to his farm.

The parade finally got under way, an hour late, and without a hero. The Reception Committee rode in Judge Draper's fine carriage. Sam and his friends marched, right alongside the brass band. But it was not nearly as exciting as they had expected.

The rest of the Fourth of July was just like every other Fourth of July in Hannibal. The Ladies' Quilting Circle served a picnic dinner in Draper's Meadow. Sam Clemens ate too much cold fried chicken, and barely managed to stuff down two helpings of strawberry short-cake on top of it.

On the afternoon excursion across the river to the Illinois shore, he didn't want to do much. He and Will Bowen and John Briggs

just hung over the rail, looking at the muddy water churning round the little stern-wheel ferryboat *Hannibal*.

In the evening, the blacksmith set off fireworks from the levee. Sam Clemens and Tom Blankenship watched a rocket burst into stars over the dark Mississippi River.

"You know what, Sam?" Tom said after a long silence. "That old redcoat man didn't look to me like anybody's enemy."

"That's exactly what I was thinking all day," Sam admitted.

"I been feeling kind of mean about him," Tom said.

"Me, too. Let's you and me get up early tomorrow morning and hike out to his farm to visit him." Sam cheered up as soon as he had a new plan.

"That's what I was fixing to do. I snagged his duds out of the store a while back. They

was right by that open window on the side,"
Tom said. "I reckon he'll need them."

"And we can take a little bucket and pick
him some wild strawberries on the way," Sam
said cheerfully. "After all, likely 't isn't his
fault he was born a redcoat."

CHAPTER SEVEN

Summertime Is a Good Time

 SAM and Tom found the ancient redcoat a very nice old man, even if he wasn't any hero. He didn't seem to remember much about what had happened the day before.

"Likely his memory is 'most wore out at his age," Sam whispered to Tom.

The old man was very glad to get his work-clothes back. He was wearing his red tunic and kept trying to brush off the bits of earth that clung to it after a morning's chores.

"Now I take this real kindly of you boys," he said. "Just set a spell out here till I fetch a pitcher of milk from the springhouse. You look plumb tuckered out."

So they all sat in the shade of an apple tree and he shared their present of wild strawberries with them. Pretty soon he began to nod, and when they left he was sound asleep.

The boys found the road back to Hannibal twice as hot and twice as dusty, and three times as long as it had seemed coming out. But they both felt better for making the trip.

When Sam got home, his face was white under his freckles. His legs were shaky, just the way they had been on the first day out of bed after measles. His mother was worried.

"I declare to goodness, Sam, you haven't got a lick of sense to get as tired as this. What have you been up to?"

"Nothing special, Ma." Sam didn't want to talk about the old redcoat right now. "I've only been loafing around."

Mrs. Clemens sat right down and wrote to her sister, Patsy, who lived out in the country about thirty miles from Hannibal. She wrote about how sick Sam had been, and how Hannibal was so hot and all choked with jimson weeds and dust in the middle of summer. She sent the letter off by the stage driver the very next morning.

The answer came quickly, but it was not a letter. Aunt Patsy's husband, Uncle John

Quarles, just sent a man with a buggy to bring Sam right out to the farm. Mrs. Clemens made Sam wash his ears and put on his clean shirt, though Sam saw no reason for wasting time on such foolishness.

"I'm clean enough, Ma. Where's Sandy? I want him to come along."

"Now, Sam, Sandy has a lot of chores to do since he lost so much time being sick."

"But, Ma—that's not fair!" Sam protested. "It was on account of me Sandy got sick. He's still every bit as shaky as I am. He'd be pale, too, if he could."

Mrs. Clemens argued. So did Sam. Mrs. Clemens gave in.

"I never saw such a stubborn boy, Sam. Pure kin to a Missouri mule."

Sam grinned. "Sandy can come?"

"Oh, all right—but both of you hustle or you'll never get to the farm today."

Sam and Sandy were ready in a couple of shakes. And Sam managed to smuggle Minniecat out of the house, hidden in a basket under his clean jeans. On the long drive, he wondered if Uncle John was going to mind having an extra cat boarding with him.

He need not have worried. John Quarles was a big, easygoing man, as rich as Sam's father was poor. He had a five-hundred-acre farm and a hundred men working on it. He had a comfortable house. And he loved nothing better than to see it crowded to the garret with children and company and hound dogs.

Along toward sunset, Uncle John met the buggy at the gate. His eyes twinkled when he saw a tiny head poking out of the basket.

"So this is Minniecat," he said when Sam told him her name. "She looks more like Minniekitten to me. But she's welcome. So is your little Sandy here. Come along, all three of you. We'll have to see if Aunt Hanner's cooking can't put a little meat on all your bones."

Sam's eyes opened wide when Uncle John led him into the dining room. He had never seen such a feast before, except on the Fourth of July. But this was the everyday supper of the Quarles family.

Platters were heaped with fried chicken and roast pig. Corn on the cob and tiny pink new potatoes dripped with butter. Jam and pickles, hot cornbread and pitchers of buttermilk crowded the table till there was only room for a ring of plates round the edge. Pies waited on a sideboard, and a watermelon cooled in a wooden tub of water.

Sam was almost overcome. He was used to eating boiled beans and bacon for dinner, and fried mush for supper. He licked his lips. Then he felt shy, with a lot of people smiling at him.

And there was a crowd! Aunt Patsy and Uncle John had eight children. And there were three strangers who had stopped to water their horses and had been urged to stay for a bite to eat. A girl of Sam's age made room for him next to her.

"Don't you remember me, Sammy?" she asked. "I'm your cousin Tabitha. Kinfolks can call me Puss."

Sam's shyness soon wore off. Before long he was up to mischief as usual. One day his aunt Patsy sat down with her sewing basket in her

lap. Sam watched her closely. Suddenly she screamed. Sam headed for the outdoors. It seemed to him like a good time to inspect the watermelon patch.

Aunt Patsy got her breath back and took her sewing basket out to the yard. When she turned it upside down, darning wool and pink floss spilled onto the grass. So did the harmless

[69]

little green garter snake that had been curled up in it.

"That Sam!" Aunt Patsy muttered. "And me worrying because he was sickly. This isn't going to be a peaceful summer."

Then she laughed. She was Mrs. Clemens' sister, and another redhead. So she understood Sam pretty well.

The watermelons grew among tall corn. Sam hid in the corn till he was sure Aunt Patsy wasn't chasing him. Then he went off past the smokehouse and barns, looking for his cousin Puss. He climbed the honeysuckle-covered fence into the orchard. He tested an apple and then a peach to see if they were ripening.

"Reckon maybe I better not chance it again," he told himself.

Only day before yesterday he had learned how lively green apples and peaches can act in a boy's inside.

He left the orchard and crossed the brook and went through woods where squirrels chattered at him. Under the last of the black walnut trees, his cousin Puss Quarles was waiting for him.

"Did you catch it from Mama?" Puss asked. "I didn't dast wait 'cause I'd have laughed right out. Then Mama would have guessed you were up to some devilment."

"Well, I didn't catch it," Sam bragged. "She yelled, too."

"You shouldn't scare my mama," Puss said, giggling.

"Let's swing," Sam suggested. "I'll start you."

Sam and Puss swung high and long in the swings made of braided hickory sapling bark. Sam was forty feet in the air when he saw a Negro woman crossing the brook to get the cows.

They "let the old cat die," and Sam raced across the pasture. Puss followed him and their whoops set the cows running off with their bells jangling. The woman's voice followed them both.

"I'm a-going to tell on you rapscallions!" she called. "Scaring the cows that way!"

Sam and Puss didn't believe she would do it. But they thought they might as well go home the long way round, by the road. Before they reached the house, a thunderhead of cloud had come up over the prairie. And lightning zigzagged over their heads.

The storm left the air cool enough for a fire after supper, and all the children gathered round the huge hearth. Sandy sprawled with the hounds, and Minniecat curled up between the front paws of a motherly old dog.

Firelight shone faintly on the oak floor, which was freckled with black holes where embers had jumped out. The sugary sap bubbling out of the flaming hickory logs was not wasted. The children took turns scraping it off and eating it.

Sitting on a splint-bottomed stool, old Uncle Ned was telling stories. Sam already knew most of them, for Uncle Ned had been the Clemenses' man-of-all-work until they grew too poor to keep him. This evening ended, as such evenings always did, with a ghost story.

"Which one do you all want tonight?" Uncle Ned asked.

"The Golden Arm!" Sam shouted quickly.

He had heard that tale over and over, but he never tired of it. And he knew that Sandy had never heard it yet. Sam wanted to watch him when he did.

Uncle Ned waited till there wasn't a sound except for the hissing fire and the snoring of the oldest hound.

"Once 'pon a time," he began, "there was a man. The man had a wife, and she had a arm of pure gold. She died one day and they buried her in the graveyard. But her husband was a greedy man. He got to brooding about that golden arm going to waste. One dark night, he went out creepsome with a shovel. He dug his wife up. He cut off her golden arm and took it along home."

"That's right," Sam put in. "It happened exactly like Uncle Ned tells, Sandy."

Sandy shivered and hugged one of the hounds.

"So-o-o," Uncle Ned went on, "next night this man waked up. There in the moonlight, he saw a white ghost. It shook and it shivered over him. It was his wife, and she says:

" 'Wha-r-r-s my golden arm? Wh-a-r-r-r-s my golden arm? Wh-h-a-a-r-r-r-s my golden arm?' "

Uncle Ned repeated this blood-curdling question to each of his listeners. His eyes gleamed in the firelight. His fingers crooked like claws as he bent forward. There was an

awful pause as he waited each time for an answer that didn't come.

At last he pounced at Sandy, with a great
shout.

" 'YOU've got it!' she says. And she done
tore him *all* to pieces!"

Sandy's yell came up to Sam's best hopes.

"That's how to tell it," Sam said to himself.
"Exactly like Uncle Ned does. I'm going to
remember to tell stories that way."

CHAPTER EIGHT

The Mystery of the Cave

THE best of summers must end. Persimmons were ripe and sumac was turning red when Sam went home to Hannibal.

"Did anything happen while I was away?" he asked Henry.

"Nothing much," his brother replied. "Judge Draper's team ran away. There was a fire at the sawmill. And Pa decided to raise silkworms. I think he's giving it up, though. Our mulberries aren't the kind they like to feed on, or something."

"Why did Pa want to raise silkworms?" Sam asked.

"He said there's money in it if you get started right. Oh, some new folks named Hawkins moved in across the way. They're kin to the *Hannibal*'s captain."

[75]

"Any boys?" Sam asked. He thought if he had a friend who was related to a ferryboat skipper he might get some free rides.

Henry said there was only a girl. Sam lost interest.

"How's Tom Blankenship?" he wanted to know.

"Nobody's seen Tom for weeks," Henry said. "He disappeared about the same time Injun Joe did."

"Who's Injun Joe?"

"He's an Osage. And he's redder-headed than you are."

"Injuns don't have red hair," Sam protested.

"This one does," Henry said. "About the end of July, a bunch of cattlemen brought him to Hannibal. They left him behind when they went downriver. He got scalped by a Pawnee Injun one time when he was ten years old. So he wears a bright red wig to cover up his scars."

"I want to see him," Sam said.

"Nobody knows where he's gone," Henry explained. "For a while he earned his eats toting carpetbags from the levee to Coleman's

Tavern. And he was sleeping in that big hollow sycamore tree down by Bear Creek."

Sam wanted to talk about Injun Joe some more, but Henry had been saving his biggest news for the last.

"We're changing schools," he told Sam. "Day after tomorrow we can start at Mr. Cross's. He knows a lot more than Miss Mary Ann, so I'm glad."

Sam groaned. As far as he was concerned, Mr. Cross was worse than Miss Mary Ann. He was stronger than any old maid. And he used a stick instead of a switch.

Sam spent most of his time next day trying to work up a sickness that would get him out of going to school. But Mrs. Clemens didn't believe that Sam was coming down with a fit or a fever. So he went to school on Monday morning.

But the moment he saw the new girl sitting across the aisle, he stopped fretting.

Laura Hawkins was the prettiest girl he had ever seen. She had big blue eyes and yellow pigtails tied with red bows. Sam was still staring at her when Mr. Cross called the class to order for a spelling bee.

[77]

"I want to see how much my new pupils know," the teacher said.

Spelling was the only subject Sam Clemens ever shone in. He was just a natural born speller. When only two pupils were left standing, Sam was one of them. Laura was the other.

"February!" Mr. Cross read from his list of words.

Sam could spell it backwards. Or standing on his head.

"F-e-b—uh—u-a-r-y," he said, choking a little.

"F-e-b-R-u-a-r-y," Laura Hawkins put him right.

Laura did not guess that she won the spelling bee because Sam was being gallant. Henry knew, though. All the way home Henry kept singing, "Sam's got a girl! Sam's got a girl!"

Sam began to spend a lot of time halfway between his home and the Hawkins house. He showed off for Laura, turning cartwheels in the road, and balancing his slingshot on his nose.

Laura pretended not to notice him at first. But by the end of the week, Sam was bringing her the last of the mulberries. And when he got a Winesap apple, he gave her the core with a lot left on it.

Will Bowen and John Briggs were disgusted. Henry teased. Mrs. Clemens was pleased that Sam was being good, for once.

One day Laura let Sam carry her books home after school. "My uncle is taking an excursion down to the cave Saturday on his ferryboat," she said. "I've never been there. Do you know about it?"

Did Sam Clemens know about the cave?

He knew it as well as he knew Holliday's Hill, or Bear Creek, or the levee!

The limestone cave was three miles from Hannibal. It was about the best place in the world to Sam and his friends, even if they could not often get there. It was a real cave, not just a hole. It had deep passages and vaulted chambers, and ran far back into the bluffs, and down into the earth's black silence. Folks said it even ran out under the Mississippi River. It was full of mystery and danger.

"This will be Uncle Frank's last excursion trip this year," Laura said. "He's going to take me. He said I could ask anybody I wanted, too. Do you want to go, Sam?"

Sam wanted to go all right. A chance to explore the cave—and with the nicest girl he had ever known! The only wonder was that Sam got any sleep between then and Saturday.

But at last Saturday came. It was a crisp autumn day with the hills painted up like Indians on the warpath. The *Hannibal* paddled along sedately down the river. The paying passengers were all much older than Sam and Laura, and they paid very little attention to the two children.

The *Hannibal* landed them near the caverns. Then a young man began handing out tallow candles to the excursion party who were setting out to explore. He gave one to Sam and one to Laura.

"Don't you young ones get lost now," he warned them. "Stay where you can see grown folks."

"Pooh," Sam told Laura. "I bet I know this cave better than any of them. Stick with me and you'll be all right."

But before Sam quite knew how it happened, they were out of sight of the others. Not a flicker could they see of any candles except their own.

"I don't like this!" Laura's voice was quavery.

Sam didn't like it so much either, but he wasn't going to let Laura know that. They were in a cavern with a very low ceiling and sharp stalactites hung down like rocky icicles.

Then something black swooped right past Laura's face. In the flickering light of their candles, its shadow was huge on the damp limestone walls.

"*Bats!*" Laura shrieked. She tried to cover

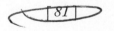

her hair with her hands. People had told her if a bat got tangled in a girl's hair, the only way to get it out was to cut off all the hair.

Either the light or Laura's scream roused dozens of other bats that had been sleeping in the cave. Suddenly the stale air was full of them. They wheeled and dove at the children. One flew right through the flame of Laura's candle. Laura shut her eyes. But she did not shut her mouth. She went right on screaming.

"Don't you cry," Sam tried to comfort her. "You're safe with me."

But Laura refused to be comforted.

The harder Sam tried to find his way back out of the cave, the more lost he became. They stumbled into one rocky cell after another that he did not remember at all. He had no idea which direction to take. He tried yelling to the excursion party. The only answer was a jeering echo.

"Look, Laura," Sam said at last. "Let's blow out your candle. That way we'll have one left if mine burns down."

Laura thought that was a terrible idea. Especially when she and Sam saw a head appear around a corner.

Shiny black eyes peered at them steadily. They were part of the ugliest face Sam had ever seen. In the dim light, its nose was sharp as a beak. The mouth was thin and tight. And the whole face was topped by a mop of startling red hair.

"G-g-ghost!" Laura Hawkins tried to go on screaming. But all that came out now was a little moan and a gulp.

"It's Injun Joe!" Sam hadn't meant to say it out loud, but the words got out by themselves.

Laura shuddered and sobbed.

"Here, take my hand," Sam whispered to her. "We'll run."

As they bolted, Injun Joe came after them at a nice easy lope. He gained on them. Sam did not know which way to turn in those weird corridors. He was losing his head completely when a voice stopped him in his tracks.

"Hey, Sam! Don't be scared. It's me. And Injun Joe won't hurt you."

The voice was Tom Blankenship's.

Tom led them through winding passages to a place where they could see the glimmering candles of the sight-seeing party. Injun Joe slouched along behind Sam and Laura. Laura clung to Sam's hand with a grip that sent pins and needles shooting all the way up his arm.

Now that his own scare was over, Sam was curious.

"What you doing in here, Tom?" he asked. "You and him?" His glance took in the tall, glum young Indian.

"We're living here," Tom said. "It's easy. We found us a back way in and out. We got a place where we can build a fire without getting all smoked up. Bats make pretty fair eating the way Injun Joe cooks them."

Laura shivered from head to foot. But Sam wished he could live here with them.

The Osage boy spoke at last. Then it was to Tom. "Them no tell?" he asked.

"I won't tell, you bet," Sam promised. "Honest Injun, I won't."

Something like a smile cracked Injun Joe's face.

"The girl no tell?" he persisted.

"I'll see she doesn't," Sam said. "Can I come back and visit you?"

Injun Joe nodded. "Alone. Girls too scary."

Sam had a little trouble with Laura on the

[*85*]

way home. She wanted to tell her uncle what had happened.

"You can't do that," Sam argued. "We promised."

"You promised, you mean," Laura insisted. "I didn't."

"Well, but it might get Tom and Injun Joe in trouble," Sam said.

"I don't care if it does. Serve them right for scaring folks," Laura said.

But at last she promised Sam she wouldn't say a word either, about what she had seen in the cave.

CHAPTER NINE

The Blood Brothers of the Black Avenger

SUNSHINE streamed through the school-room window. Sam sighed and squirmed in his seat. Mr. Cross had been giving him a bad time all the morning.

"Old Crosspatch," Sam mumbled, keeping a wary eye on the teacher. Then he began to scribble on his slate:

> "Cross by name and cross by nature,
> Cross jumped over an Irish potato."

Sam wouldn't claim that the two lines were poetry. But he liked them. He passed the slate back over his shoulder to John Briggs in the row behind.

John thought the lines were wonderful. "Write it on the board at noon," he whispered.

Sam shook his head. His ambition did not reach that far.

"Shucks," John said, "I wouldn't be scared to do it."

"All right, I dare you," Sam said.

John Briggs always took a dare. So when Mr. Cross went home to his dinner, John wrote the two lines big and clear in white chalk. He took a piece of red chalk and decorated the word *Cross* with squiggles.

At the end of the noon hour the boys and girls took their seats. They saw what John had written and all began to giggle.

Mr. Cross glanced at the blackboard. His

face soon lived up to his name. And he recognized the handwriting.

"Did you do that, John Briggs?"

"Yes, sir." There was no use denying it.

John took his beating. Sam expected the teacher to ask next who made up the lines, but he didn't. Sam wasn't used to escaping so easily. Generally, his back stayed warm from one whipping to another.

After his adventure in the cave Sam's spell of being good had soon worn off. Things had never been the same between him and Laura Hawkins since that day. Now Sam wanted nothing to do with girls. He decided to start a club that only boys could belong to. He told Will Bowen and John Briggs and Arch Fuqua about it after school.

"That's grand," Will said. "What'll we call our club?"

"I've thought up a name already," Sam replied. "We'll be the *Blood Brothers of the Black Avenger.*"

"Hey, that's a good name!" Arch Fuqua said. He cracked his big toe, and it made a hollow noise inside his new copper-toed boot. "But what does it mean?"

"Well, you know what blood brothers are," Sam explained. "Like when Injuns take a white man into their tribe, they mix up some of his blood along with some of theirs. Then he's a blood brother forever after."

"Do we have to do that?" Will asked.

"Sure we do." Sam was positive. "It wouldn't be real without we did that."

"Who'll be the Black Avenger?" John Briggs wanted to know.

"Me, of course," Sam said. " 'Cause I thought it up. We'll hold our first meeting down at the cave, with initiation and all. That way we can make Tom a member."

"Tom's all right," Will Bowen agreed. "But what about this Injun Joe that's living down there with Tom? He's bigger than us and maybe he'll think he ought to be Black Avenger his own self."

Sam didn't want that to happen. Besides, Injun Joe was still a bit scary. But the matter of Injun Joe settled itself. The Osage boy came back to Hannibal and got a steady job working for his keep down at Coleman's Tavern.

On Saturday morning the boys went overland to the caves. Sam showed them a slit in the earth between two boulders, where they could drop right into the cavern.

"Tom showed me this way in when I was over the other day," he explained.

Tom was glad to see his friends. He thought the club was wonderful and that Sam was awfully smart to think it up by himself.

Sam called his meeting to order in a dim cavern room where the only light came from a small fire Tom had built. Sam pulled a grubby piece of paper out of his pocket and read aloud what he had written on it.

"We who sign with our blood are Blood Brothers of the Black Avenger. The password is BLOOD. We swear to be true to our Black Avenger and stick to club rules. We swear never to tell any girls about this club. If we break this rule we hope to drop dead."

"That about covers it, I reckon," Sam said. He made a small cut on his little finger and passed his Barlow knife to the others. Each boy cut his finger enough to make it bleed. Then they mixed up all their blood together, and signed their names to the paper with it.

> Sam Clemens—the Black Avenger
> Will Bowen
> John Briggs
> Arch Fuqua

"You can make an X, Tom. We'll know it's you," Sam said.

"I don't have to," Tom replied. "I been practicing and I can write the new name you gave me real good."

So Tom Blankenship signed *FINN*. Sam was proud of him.

"This is a fine place for meetings," John said. "Only trouble is, it's so far we can't come very often."

"How about my hogshead down at the tanyard for a clubhouse?" Tom suggested. "I'm fixing to go back to Hannibal to live anyhow. It's awful cold and wet here now at night. And bats don't taste so good when I cook them alone."

"I move we take Tom up on that," said the Black Avenger.

The members agreed and the first meeting was over.

Sam Clemens thought the Black Avenger should be like Robin Hood. At the next meeting he told his blood brothers they should rob the rich and give to the poor.

"There ain't any rich folks in Hannibal but Judge Draper!" Will exclaimed.

"I don't want to steal from the judge," Tom protested. "He always lets me camp out in his barn whenever I like."

"Blood Brothers," the Black Avenger said, "Tom's right. We couldn't go robbing a nice old man like that. I propose we spend our time digging for treasure till a rich stranger turns up."

But digging was hard work. And soon the ground froze so hard they couldn't do it at all. For the winter months, the blood brothers did mostly what every other boy in Hannibal was doing. They coasted on homemade sleds. They slid on creaking black ice that covered the river. They got into mischief.

There were great doings in town in the spring of 1845. The little town incorporated itself as a city. Norval Brady's father, who had been a carpenter, became the first mayor.

The new mayor and his officials took their duties earnestly. They passed laws at every meeting. They passed a law against gambling. And another law against letting pigs run loose in the streets as they had always done before. At last they passed a law against playing any kind of game on Sundays.

That law was too much for the Black Avenger and his blood brothers. They started going to Holliday's Hill every Sunday morning. High up on the green slope, they played every kind of game they could think of, while church bells clanged across the valley.

The hill rose steep above the road along which farm families drove to church. And up where the boys played, there were a lot of loose stones lying around.

One Sunday Will kicked a rock, by accident. It plunged downhill and shot across the road a few yards in front of a wagon filled with people.

"Golly!" Sam said happily as he watched the horses rear and heard the churchgoers scream. "Just look at that!"

The next Sunday the blood brothers sent another rock down the hill, and not by chance. It worked fine. But it was the sort of prank that builds up to real danger before you know it. Because they were excited, Sam and his friends lost every bit of sense in their heads.

"Mighty peculiar," people began saying. "Rocks always coming loose on Sundays and never on weekdays."

They reported it to the river patrol police. The river patrol began to keep a watch on the hill.

"I reckon we better lay low for a spell," the Black Avenger told his blood brothers the next Sunday.

But then a rock the size of a stagecoach caught Sam's eye. Its position was perfect if they could only get it started down. And it would be a glorious sight to watch the boulder smash a hundred yards in front of some unsuspecting churchgoer.

"I propose the blood brothers have one last rock rolling," Sam said. "The biggest rock rolling ever seen in these parts."

Loosening the boulder was a heavier job than the boys had counted on. They borrowed some picks and shovels which workmen left lying around the quarry and worked for several Sundays.

Then while they were digging one Sunday morning, the rock suddenly came loose. They were not exactly ready for it. Nobody was in sight except John Hannicks. As drayman, he drove a fine team of horses on weekdays. But on Sunday he had only his own elderly mule.

"Shucks," Sam said. "Our work's all going to be wasted."

It was not quite wasted, however. They had planned for an exciting end to their rock rolling. And they had excitement enough while it lasted. John Briggs was just handing Will the pick when Sam gave a yell.

"Watch out! She's a-coming!"

Will jumped, and she came. At first the huge boulder kept to the ground, rolling faster and faster. Halfway down the hill, it hit a tree and cut it off clean.

John Hannicks heard a noise and looked up. Wildly, he tried to whip up his mule. But the old mule balked.

The boys could only stare at the rock which was making longer leaps with every bound. It looked as if the drayman must surely be killed. Then the rock would hit the cooper shop across the road.

They wanted to run, to get away fast and far. But their knees seemed turned to jelly. They could only stand there, just watching. The breath stuck in their throats. Their mouths hung open and their eyes were popping with horror.

Suddenly, the boulder struck another rock not far above the road. Sam could hardly believe his eyes. With a mighty bound, the big stone sailed right over John Hannicks and his mule. It landed in soft dirt, half burying itself.

Only a corner of the boulder touched the cooper shop, which was empty on Sunday. But that corner wrecked the whole building.

For quite a while the boys just stood dizzy and silent. It was Sam who first found words.

"I don't reckon," he said slowly, "that this here is a very *safe* game."

His blood brothers agreed that it was not safe. They were realizing how close they had come to killing a man.

Will Bowen thought maybe they ought to
go along to church this morning. It seemed
only fitting to give thanks that they had been
saved from becoming murderers.

Sam and Arch and John Briggs were willing
to go. But Tom Blankenship looked unhappy.

"I can't go in no church," he said. "Not in
these rags. It wouldn't show respect. Besides,
they'd throw me out."

The others had never given a thought to

Tom's dirty old clothes before. But they saw now that he was right.

"Don't worry, Tom," Sam told his friend. "We won't none of us go to church. Blood brothers stick together."

A minute later, he added. "But I don't think we'll roll any more rocks."

They never did roll any more rocks down Holliday's Hill, but during the next couple of years they got into plenty of other mischief. And Sam was usually the leader.

Then one March day in 1847 Sam's father went to a neighboring town on some business. On his way back to Hannibal, he was caught

in a sleet storm. He and his horse were both encased in ice when they reached home. And five days later, Mr. Clemens died of pneumonia.

On the day of the funeral, the ice and snow had turned to a steady downpour of rain. Sam had never seen such a dreary place as the graveyard with its dead weeds and soggy cedar trees.

The thick crepe veils that his mother and Pamela wore were wet and limp. And Sam's clothes got soaked while he listened to the preacher praising Pa's honesty and deep sense of duty. The preacher talked about Pa's courage in the face of misfortune, too. Sam had never thought of his father like that before, but he figured the preacher must be right.

"Maybe Pa didn't enjoy being stern and cross," Sam thought. "He might even have wanted to laugh the way other folks did. It wasn't his fault that things never turned out right for him."

Henry was crying. Sam wished he could cry, too. It might make him feel better. Henry had always been a good boy, and he had made Pa proud of him. So Henry really had nothing to bother his conscience. With Sam it was different.

Sam worried and fretted about this all day. That night, he lay in bed tossing, thinking about how he had disappointed his father.

Later he began to walk in his sleep again. It was the first time he had done that since he almost killed John Hannicks with the big rock.

Without waking up, Sam wrapped himself in his sheet. He went to the room which his mother and Pamela shared. And his white fig-

[*101*]

ure nearly frightened them into fits when it loomed up before them.

Pamela was sure it was Pa's ghost. She buried her head in the quilts. But Mrs. Clemens looked a second time. If the ghost of her husband was walking, she felt pretty sure it would not have shrunk to the size of an eleven-year-old boy.

"Sam," she said, "come here!"

Sam obeyed, still asleep. Mrs. Clemens put her arms round him. Sam woke up to find his mother hugging him.

"Oh, Ma," he sobbed, "I feel bad. Awful bad. 'Cause I was always a-worrying Pa."

"I know, Sam. But what's done is done. We can't any of us live the past over again, no matter how much we want to."

Sam snuffled.

"But we can try to do better in the future, Sam," his mother went on. "Will you promise me to try?"

"I will, Ma. I promise." Sam's sobs died away to hiccups. "I'll go to work and make money for you, Ma. I'll do anything—just *anything*—if only you don't make me go back to school."

Mrs. Clemens sighed. "All right, Sam. You don't have to go to school any more."

She could no longer afford to send him to school in any case.

CHAPTER TEN

Sam Clemens, Printer's Devil

SAM tried hard to get a real job. For a few weeks he was errand boy at the Wildcat Store. Then for a while he held nervous, stomping horses for the blacksmith. He worked one day at the tannery, but the smell made him sick. He tried to enlist to fight in the Mexican War, but nobody wanted a twelve-year-old soldier that year.

At last he decided he'd be a printer like his big brother Orion, who worked in St. Louis. So he signed on as apprentice in the office of Mr. Joseph Ament's weekly newspaper, the *Missouri Courier*.

One day he was standing over a high desk when Pet McMurry, the journeyman printer, called to him.

"Got the type lice out of that box yet, Sam?"

"Not yet," Sam admitted. "But I'm looking for them."

All Sam could see in the box was a lot of old broken type stuck together with some tallow. There were no lice at all. He wondered where the pesky insects could be hiding. He didn't want to disappoint Pet McMurry. The breezy young journeyman was Sam's new hero.

Sam admired everything about Pet from his plug hat to his tallow-shined shoes. He thought Pet's bright green swallowtail coat with the big brass buttons was a real treat to see.

Sam was feeling uncomfortable about his own clothes for the first time in his life. As an apprentice, he got no wages. But Mr. Ament had promised him his board and two suits of clothes a year. Now he was wearing the first of these suits, a hand-me-down of Mr. Ament's. It was so big it hardly touched the boy inside it.

"It's sort of like a circus tent," Sam thought.

He kept hitching up his sleeves so he could use his hands hunting for the type lice. When he bent over the box, his chin slipped down

[105]

into his loose collar. He could get lost in that shirt right up to his eyebrows.

Learning to be a printer was hard enough. It was worse when he had to swim up out of his clothes to see what he was doing. But already,

after a week in the office, he was feeling like a real printer. He was standing at a real desk, looking for real type lice.

The door opened with a bang and a gust of wind. Another apprentice, named Wales Mc-Cormick, blew in. Wales had been there a month longer than Sam, and he considered himself an old hand.

"What are you doing, Sammy, me sprout?" he asked.

"Looking for type lice for Mr. McMurry," Sam replied.

Wales laughed so hard he shook the desk. "That's a good one!" he exclaimed. "Pet fooled you with the oldest joke in the printing trade." Wales did not say he himself had been taken in by the same trick not long ago. "There's no such critters as type lice."

Sam's ears turned as red as his hair. This was not the first joke which had been played on him. But he meant to catch on to all these jokes. When he did, the rest of them had better look out.

Jokes were only played in the *Courier* office when the editor was out. Sam had plenty of hard work to do.

He built the fires on freezing winter mornings. He toted water from the town pump. For hours on end, he sorted type. On Saturdays he had to wet down the whole stock of paper, and turn it over on Sunday mornings. He stirred lye in the hopper. He washed the rollers and forms.

The new printer's devil not only worked in

the office. He lived there. His bed was a pallet on the printshop floor.

"I don't mind sleeping on the floor," Sam said. "But I do hate to go to bed hungry."

Mr. Ament's skinny old-maid sister kept house for the editor. She was so stingy with the food that she doled out brown sugar, grain by grain, for the apprentices' coffee.

Sam and Wales were always hungry. Sometimes they were too hungry to sleep. Then they raided the cellar for potatoes in the middle of the night and cooked them on the printing-room stove. But one day every month, they enjoyed a real meal.

"Stir your stumps, you two!" Pet McMurry would shout at them. "The ghost walked today, and we eat!"

When Pet said the ghost walked, he meant it was his payday. His pockets were heavy with silver dollars, so he took the boys down to Coleman's Tavern and really stuffed them.

Since editor Ament's temper was as sharp as his sister's long nose, it was a good thing he was away often.

"I'm going out to gather news," he always said when he left.

But it was Pet McMurry who was the real reporter for the *Courier,* as well as its printer. It was Pet McMurry who taught Sam to take pride in his new work and to turn out good clean pages of proof. When the weekly sheets came off the press, Sam folded them. He delivered them around town on Thursday morning at dawn.

One blustery Thursday morning, something happened that changed Sam's life for good. The wind whirled up a scrap of paper out of the road and plastered it against his leg. Sam shifted his heavy sack of *Missouri Couriers* and picked the scrap off his pants. He glanced at it. Then he began to read, standing right in the middle of Main Street.

"The Maid of Orleans faced her jeering captors . . ."

It was a page torn out of a book about Joan of Arc.

Sam Clemens had never heard of Joan of Arc. But those first words, all in a moment, brought her to life for him. He read down the page. He turned it over and read the other side. He forgot where he was, and what he was supposed to be doing.

The story broke off in the middle of a sentence, but Sam did not move. He was still wondering what had happened next to Joan of Arc when a yell made him jump.

"That's a good way to get yourself killed!" shouted the drayman, pulling hard on the reins to stop his team.

Sam had not heard the horses coming, though they were close enough to breathe down the back of his neck.

Now he delivered the rest of his papers in a great rush. He burst into the Clemenses' kitchen, nearly upsetting his mother as she dished up mush for Henry's breakfast.

Henry did not get a chance to taste it before Sam grabbed him right out of his chair.

"Why didn't you tell me?" he demanded.

"Let go!" Henry protested. "You're hurting. Tell you what?"

"About books!" Sam said. "Here you've gone on reading them all this time and you never told me . . ." For once, words failed Sam. He thrust the muddy page at his brother.

Henry read a couple of sentences. "Oh, I know this book. I wonder who tore it."

"Where can I get hold of the rest of it quick?" Sam wanted to know.

"Why, over at the Library Institute, of course," Henry said. "Seems funny you didn't know about it. Sometimes I wonder what you *do* know, Sam."

"Never mind that," Sam said. "I'll soon catch up with you. But I always thought books were full of dull stuff. Does Robin Hood that Pam told me about come in a book, too? And King Arthur and his knights?"

"Of course they do," Henry said.

After that day, whenever Sam could get away from the *Courier* office, he went to the Library Institute. This library was only a few shelves of books in Dr. Meredith's office over the Wildcat Store. The doctor didn't have so many books or so many patients that he could not keep track of them all.

"I'm mighty glad to see you here, Sam," the old doctor said one afternoon. "I always knew you'd be mad when you found out what you had been missing. At the rate you're going now, though, it won't be long before you've read as much as Henry."

Sam grinned and started back to the office with an armload of books. Then he saw Miss Mary Ann Newcomb walking down the street in front of him. He sprinted to catch up with her.

"Miss Mary Ann," he said, "I just wanted to thank you . . ."

"Whatever for, Sam?"

"For making me learn to read," Sam said. "I do thank you . . ."

"What's got into you now, Sam Clemens?" Miss Newcomb asked. "Are you sickening for something again? Or trying to wheedle your way out of some new devilment?"

"No, honest, it's nothing like that," Sam protested. "I just found out that reading is fun."

Miss Mary Ann shook her head. But she was smiling when she watched Sam race on ahead, clutching his books.

CHAPTER ELEVEN

A Dream Comes True

WELL, this *is* nice, Orion," Mrs. Clemens said. Her oldest son had just walked into the kitchen. While Pamela put the coffeepot on the fire, she cut a spicy apple pie into big wedges.

"It's the first time in years I've had you all home at once," Mrs. Clemens went on happily, "with you working in St. Louis and Pamela away teaching. Even Sam only gets home every other Sunday, so it's been lonesome for Henry and me. I wish this could last."

"Well, it can last so far as I'm concerned, Ma," Orion said. "You've always wanted me to run a newspaper here in Hannibal and now I've borrowed money to start. The *Courier* will have a rival."

[*114*]

"Hooray!" Sam shouted. "I'll be your reporter. My two years with Mr. Ament are up. I know as much about running a newspaper now as he does."

"You always did know a powerful lot in your own opinion," Orion told his excited brother. "I'll be my own reporter, thank you. You can work at the printing. Mind you, though, I won't be able to pay you a salary straight off."

"Oh, I'm used to that," Sam said. "I reckon your old suits will fit me better than Ament's do. And I can live here at home, so Ma will see I get enough to eat."

"That's settled," Orion agreed. "I'll take Henry on as apprentice. Now that he's eleven, it's time he went to work."

"Are you sure Hannibal is big enough to support another newspaper?" Mrs. Clemens asked. Borrowing money frightened her.

"Of course, Ma," Orion said. "The town's growing every day. I've got a printing press coming on the steamboat next week."

"We'll give folks a lot more news than the *Courier* does," Sam promised. "Bigger and better news, too!"

[*115*]

"I hope so," Mrs. Clemens was still worried. She knew Orion meant well, but he was bumbling and absent-minded. Things almost never turned out for him as he expected. However, it was done now, so there was no use fussing. And she was happy at the prospect of having her children at home. Even Pamela was going to teach in Hannibal this next year.

Orion started his newspaper and worked hard. So did his young brothers. They brought out the first issues of their newspaper with a great deal of pride and very high hopes.

Almost from the start, bad luck seemed to follow them. Fire broke out in the printshop. And the Liberty Boys Volunteer Firemen did more damage with their buckets of water than the flames did.

Shortly after that, a curious cow wandered in to see what went on in a newspaper office. Before the boys could get her out, she had chewed up two rollers and upset a case of type.

Then an epidemic of cholera broke out all along the Mississippi River. Everyone was worried about that dreaded disease, and times were bad in Hannibal. When Orion managed to get people to subscribe to his paper, they

seldom paid him in cash. Mostly they paid in
cordwood and eggs, cabbages and potatoes and
turnips. More turnips than anything else.

"I wish I never had to see another turnip as
long as I live!" Sam complained to Henry one
day.

Suddenly he had an idea. He had just heard
about a doctor in St. Louis who said turnips
were good for people, and that eating plenty
of turnips might even keep folks from catching cholera. With a little smile Sam went to
work setting type.

[*117*]

When the *Journal* came off the press the following Wednesday, Orion noticed something on the front page which he had not written himself. His eyes flashed as he read:

DON'T CATCH CHOLERA—
TAKE THE JOURNAL

An eminent medical man says eating turnips is almost sure-fire cholera prevention. As a public service, the *Journal* will give away *absolutely free* one bushel of turnips with every new, paid subscription.

DON'T DELAY. SAVE YOUR
HEALTH!

"Sam!" he cried, wildly waving a paper on which the ink was still wet. "Did you do this?"

"Yep," Sam said. "I figured it out to bring in some subscriptions and take out some turnips."

"You can't do this to my paper! It's not dignified."

"Who cares about dignity if we get rid of turnips?" Sam wanted to know. "It's got so bad we fall over turnips here every time we turn around, and Ma goes pale when she has to cook them."

But Sam had forgotten one thing. Almost all the people in Hannibal had turnips growing right in their own vegetable patches. They certainly did not need any more. Sam's notice had made them laugh, though. And laughter is good for folks who are worried.

That was the first big argument that Sam and Orion had. But it was not the last. An itch for writing took hold of Sam Clemens. Whenever he had a chance he smuggled funny little articles into print. He still liked to give himself new names, so he signed them *W. Epaminondas Adrastus Blab.*

Soon the first thing Hannibal people looked for in their *Journal* was the headline: Blabbing Town Secrets. They read Sam's little articles and laughed. But Orion didn't laugh. He always got good and mad. Since both he and Sam had redheaded tempers, they were soon fighting, hot and heavy.

"It's my paper and I'll run it my way!" Orion roared one day.

"You can run it *all* your own way. And all by yourself after this," Sam retorted. "I quit —here and now."

Grabbing his cap, he went home and told his mother he was off to St. Louis to look for a job.

"Oh, Sam," Mrs. Clemens said. "What will become of you?"

"I'll be all right, Ma. It's what will become of Orion you had better be worrying about."

Mrs. Clemens sighed. "I'm afraid you're right. Well, I'll not hold you back, Sam. But be a good boy and write me sometimes."

"I will, Ma," Sam said as he hurriedly packed his few clothes. "I'll always write you letters." It was one promise Sam knew he could keep. He liked writing letters or anything else now.

Sam was a good printer, so he found it easy

to get work. But he was restless. He stayed in St. Louis only long enough to earn money to go on to other towns. He went as far as New York just to see the big city. Then he found a job in Cincinnati. While he was there he read about some Americans who had been exploring the Amazon River in South America. They had been looking for the source of the great river. But they had not been able to find it.

"I'll bet I could," Sam told himself. "Most likely they weren't old river hands like I am. I think I'll try it."

Sam began to calculate. He had thirty dollars. That was more than enough to get to New Orleans, fifteen hundred miles away. There he ought to find a ship sailing for South America.

He packed his satchel, bought his passage, and started downriver on a steamboat named *Paul Jones*. They went down the Ohio River and into the Mississippi. For two weeks the scarred old steamboat zigzagged back and forth across the water, stopping at towns on both sides of the wide river.

The other passengers found the slow trip

very tedious but Sam loved every mile of it. As soon as he was on the river, all his old restlessness left him.

Sam spent most of his time on the hurricane deck, watching the man in the pilot house. There were two pilots on the boat. Each was on duty four hours at a time. One of them was named Bixby.

Mr. Bixby was not a big man, but he had an air of calm command that Sam longed to imitate. Sam talked to him about his work on the river whenever he could, but Mr. Bixby did not encourage visitors in his pilot house.

At last the *Paul Jones* reached New Orleans. Sam stepped ashore with the other passengers and looked about. An old riverman was leaning against a bale of cotton. Sam spoke to him.

"Excuse me, sir. How soon is a ship sailing from here to the mouth of the Amazon River?"

"The Amazon?" The old riverman shifted a plug of tobacco in his cheek. "I don't remember any boat that ever went there. Course, one might some day if you want to wait around for it, ten or twelve years maybe."

"I don't remember any boat that ever went there"

With only nine dollars left in his pocket and ten years to wait for a boat, Sam decided to give up his trip to the Amazon. The Mississippi River was good enough for him. After all, it was *his* river. Hadn't he dreamed of being a pilot on the Mississippi? It was high time he set about making that dream come true.

In those days river pilots were allowed to take along boys who wanted to become pilots. Such boys were called cubs, and the steamboat companies gave them free board. Free board and a chance to learn to navigate the river were just what Sam wanted now. He began to search for Mr. Bixby, and found him standing outside the steamboat company's office.

"Will you teach me to be a pilot, please, sir?" he asked.

"No, I don't want any more cubs," Mr. Bixby said. "Most of them are more nuisance than they're worth."

"I wouldn't be a nuisance," Sam promised.

"I said I don't want any more cubs," Mr. Bixby growled. "Now get out!"

Sam got out, but he did not give up. For three days he followed Mr. Bixby around asking the same question. At last he had the pilot completely worn out. "All right, Sam," Mr. Bixby said wearily. "I'll teach you the river from here to St. Louis for five hundred dollars."

"Five *hundred*—" Sam's heart dropped into his boots. He had not known he'd have to pay to become a cub pilot.

Mr. Bixby smiled. He had taken a liking to this young man who shared his own feeling for the river. "You can pay me out of your wages when you're a licensed pilot," he said.

When the *Paul Jones* backed out of her New Orleans wharf that afternoon, Sam already felt like a pilot. He had had experience around Hannibal with canoes and log rafts and sailing boats. He didn't think it would be hard to steer a steamer up and down and across the river just by turning a big wheel.

But by evening, Sam realized that there was a lot more to being a pilot than just holding the wheel. He found he could not obey the simplest command properly. He did his best, but Mr. Bixby told him a number of things, and he simply couldn't keep them straight in his head. It seemed as if he couldn't keep *anything* straight.

"My boy," Mr. Bixby said, "you get your-self a little notebook and put down everything I say to you. You've got thirteen hundred miles of river to learn until you know it like ABC.

"You'll have to know every rock and shoal and sounding. You'll have to learn the real shape of this river and remember it at all times. If you don't, you'll be fooled by your own eyes, because it looks different in daylight and at night, different in moonlight and fog and rain."

"Yes, sir," Sam said, hoping he understood all this.

"Now, what's the name of the first point above New Orleans?" Mr. Bixby asked.

"I—I don't know, sir."

"You—don't—know!" Mr. Bixby mim-icked Sam's slow drawl. He was a kind man, but he was a nervous one, too. When he was angry he shuffled from one side of the wheel to the other, as if the floor was hot.

"No, sir!" Sam admitted miserably.

"You're the stupidest dunderhead I ever saw, so help me Moses!" Mr. Bixby declared.

"You don't know enough to pilot a cow down a lane."

Sam groaned. "I reckon you're right, sir," he said in despair. "Give me a slush-bucket and brush. I'm only fit to be a roustabout. I haven't got brains enough to be a pilot. If I had, I wouldn't have the strength to carry them around. Not unless I went on crutches."

"Drop that!" Mr. Bixby advised Sam briskly. "When I say I'll teach a man this river, I mean it. I'll teach you the river if it kills you."

CHAPTER TWELVE

A Cub Pilot Grows Up

LEARNING the Mississippi River did not kill Sam. He bought a notebook that was soon filled with names of towns, points, islands, and shoals. In those days there were neither buoys nor lighthouses to guide pilots. But after a while Sam knew so much that he could shut his eyes and see any point on the river clearly outlined in his mind.

When Mr. Bixby left the old *Paul Jones,* Sam packed his satchel and went along to one of the biggest and finest ships on the river. Her pilot house had shiny brasswork and red and gold window curtains. It was so high that Sam Clemens felt as if he were standing on top of Holliday's Hill back in Hannibal.

One matchless summer day he stood at the

wheel, feeling every inch an experienced pilot. He wore his hat jauntily on the back of his red hair. Two young lady passengers on the hurricane deck were watching him with admiration. Life was wonderful.

"I'm going below," Mr. Bixby announced. "Can you run the next crossing alone?"

Sam nodded. That crossing from Tennessee to the Arkansas side was perfectly plain.

"I can run it with my eyes shut," he said.

"Don't do that," Mr. Bixby advised him. "How much water is there in it?"

"Why, sir, you couldn't get bottom there with a church steeple," Sam declared.

Mr. Bixby left. The young ladies on the hurricane deck could see Sam Clemens piloting this big ship all by himself.

But presently the captain stepped out beside the girls. The chief mate appeared. A couple of deckhands showed up. So did the purser. Everybody looked uneasy.

"Where is Mr. Bixby?" the captain called.

Sam's imagination was never asleep. He began to imagine dangers he couldn't see. He reached for the bell-rope to signal the engine room to slow up. But he dropped it again. He did not want the engineer to think he didn't know his job.

"Starboard lead there!" captain and mate sang out together. "Give us a sounding. And quick about it!"

That give Sam a shock. Thinking there must be danger to starboard, he swung the wheel over to port.

"D-e-e-p four!" came the leadsman's call.

That meant only twenty-four feet of water in what he had supposed was a bottomless crossing! Terror took Sam's breath away. He didn't have time to get it back because the leadsman's calls kept on coming, and getting worse and worse.

"Mark three! Quarter less three! Half twain!"

Half twain meant only fifteen feet of water under the boat. Sam almost pulled the bell-rope out to make the engineer stop the engines. He didn't know of another thing he could do.

"Mark twain!" came the call. Then, "Nine and a half feet!"

The ship needed nine feet of water to stay afloat. Sam's hands shook so he couldn't ring the bell again. He rushed to the speaking tube.

"Ben!" he yelled to the engineer. "If you love me, Ben, *back* her! Quick, Ben! Back the living daylights out of her!"

Then Mr. Bixby sauntered up. From the audience on the hurricane deck came a thundergust of laughter. Sam realized that Mr. Bixby had been playing a trick on him. He felt bitter about it.

"I'll never hear the end of this!" he complained.

"Well, you won't hear the end of it soon,"

Mr. Bixby agreed amiably. "In fact, I hope you won't. I want this experience to teach you something. Didn't you *know* there was no shoal there?"

"Yes, sir, I did," Sam admitted.

"Then you should not let anybody shake your confidence in that knowledge. Remember that. And another thing, don't lose your nerve when you get in a tight place. It never helps matters."

It was a good lesson, learned the hard way. For months, Sam had to listen to words that he came to dislike very heartily.

"Oh, Ben," members of the crew would sing out when they saw him. "Ben, if you *love* me, back her!"

CHAPTER THIRTEEN

Sam Clemens Becomes Mark Twain

OLDTIMERS began to say that Sam Clemens was one of the best pilots on the whole Mississippi. Mr. Bixby was proud of him.

The river meant a lot to Sam. He expected to spend the rest of his life on it. But when he was twenty-six years old, trouble started in the United States between the North and the South that put an end to all regular shipping on the river.

Many people in the southern states kept slaves. Many people in the North thought this was wrong. At last the southern states decided to break away from the Union and set up a government of their own. The people in the North were determined that the Union should not be broken up. And so the Civil War had begun.

Sam was very troubled when he went home to see his mother. Missouri had not left the Union with other southern states. But Will Bowen and John Briggs and a lot of Sam's other friends were enlisting in the Confederate Army to fight against the Union.

"I can't do that, Ma," Sam told Mrs. Clemens. "I think Abraham Lincoln is absolutely right. Slavery is wicked and all people ought to be free. But I can't go fighting against my best friends. I wouldn't be any good as a soldier if I was always scared I'd kill Will or John or somebody like that."

"I don't believe in slavery either," Orion said.

Orion's newspaper hadn't lasted long after Sam left it. Now he had another job.

"Pa's rich cousin in St. Louis has fixed it up for me to be Territorial Secretary of Nevada," he went on.

"Why, that's fine!" Sam exclaimed. "That's sort of an Acting Governor, isn't it? If you work hard, by the time Nevada becomes a state you might be elected Governor."

"It's a real honor," Orion said, "but I don't have enough money to get there. The fare costs all of a hundred and fifty dollars."

"That's easy," Sam told him. "I've got three hundred dollars. We'll both go west and I'll make my fortune mining. They say there's an awful lot of silver out in that Comstock Lode."

The two brothers set out by Overland Stage for Carson City, the capital of Nevada. It was a dusty trip behind sixteen galloping horses. The stage never stopped except to change horses or to give the passengers time to eat. They traveled west over billowing plains and across the Rocky Mountains that were still snow-capped in July. In nineteen days they covered seventeen hundred miles.

Sam found Carson City a real wild-west boom town. The buildings were ramshackle. Streets were thick with dust. But horses galloped through them wearing pure silver harnesses and scattering the dirt from solid silver shoes. Pack trains and cowboys jostled Indians, miners, and Chinese fruit peddlers from California. Bankers and gamblers bumped yelling newsboys and organ-grinders.

"You've got your work cut out for you if you're going to try to govern a place as wild as this," Sam told Orion.

"I can see that." Orion was gloomy already. "I only hope you make good at mining. Take care of yourself, Sam."

Sam bought a blanket and some grub to carry rolled up in it. He had hoped to get a burro, but his money ran out. So he set out on foot for the silver diggings.

After hearing men talk in Carson City, Sam had thought there was silver any place you wanted to dig for it. He soon found this was far from true. The best claims in the rich Comstock Lode had been staked out long ago. Other miners who had not found silver were just waiting to sell or rent their claims to greenhorn prospectors like Sam.

Sam was not lucky at mining. He formed a partnership with an old blacksmith and two young lawyers. Through a long, hard winter, the four of them toiled with pick and shovel, finding barely enough silver to keep them working at it.

Now and then they moved on to new claims, hoping for better luck. They traveled through sandstorm and snow. An Indian war had just ended, and they passed new graves and the charred ruins of shacks. Once a pack of wolves chased them. Luckily, just when they ran out of bullets, the wolves got discouraged and loped off in another direction.

They all hated the alkali grit that got into their clothes and blankets, and into salt pork and sourdough flapjacks. Their backs were sore. Their hands were blistered. But somehow Sam managed to laugh. He could always make his comrades laugh, too, with his "long talk."

And no matter how bad things were, Sam wrote funny letters. And Orion showed them to the publisher of a newspaper called the *Territorial Enterprise*.

"Now that's the kind of writing I want in my newspaper," the publisher said. "I'd like your brother to work for me."

Then he wrote to Sam, offering him a job. Sam got the letter when he was near Aurora, one hundred and thirty miles away, and very sick and tired of mining. It didn't take him long to decide to be a newspaperman.

On a hot August afternoon, the editor of the *Enterprise* looked up when a travel-stained figure came into the office. There was no guessing the age of the man who loosened a blanket roll and dropped into a chair. He wore a rusty slouch hat on tangled reddish hair. He had no coat. His trousers hung down over his boot tops. A tawny beard, gray with alkali dust, fell halfway to his collar. In his belt he carried a navy revolver.

"Can I do something for you?" the editor asked.

The man gave him a faraway look. "My starboard leg seems to be unshipped," he drawled. "It would take about a hundred yards of line to do anything for me. I've walked clear from Aurora and I think I'm falling to pieces."

Then he added, even more slowly, "My name is Clemens. I've come to write for the paper."

The editor smiled.

"When do you want to start work?" he asked.

"Show me a desk and I'll begin now," Sam said. He did not know that with these words he was starting his greatest career.

Several months later, Sam Clemens sat in front of his scarred desk. He was chewing the handle of his pen. "Now that I'm a real re-

"I've come to write for the paper"

porter," he told himself, "I think I'll give myself a new name. This time I want a name I'll stick to."

He stared out at the road where the alkali dust was still thick between patches of dirty February snow. Right now he was pretty homesick for clean green country and a big wide river.

"Mark Twain!" he said out loud, remembering his steamboat days on the Mississippi. "By golly, Mark Twain is going to be my name from here on out!"

CHAPTER FOURTEEN

Mark Twain Becomes a Famous Name

IT HAD been raining all day in the California hills. Now the sky was clear, but the mud was thick at Angel's Mining Camp.

Sam Clemens struggled up a slope where his partner, Jim Gillis, was looking for gold. The water in the pail which he was carrying slopped out over his legs and feet. Sam set down the pail. For a moment he wished he were back in the office of the *Territorial Enterprise*.

He had stayed there only a few months. Then he had made up his mind to become a free-lance newspaperman, so that he could write whatever he wanted to and sell it to any newspaper that would buy it. For a while he had done free-lance writing in San Francisco.

But only for a while. Suddenly he had decided to try mining again.

"And now I'm through with mining," he thought, picking up the pail. "This is the last pail of water I'm going to tote up this hill."

A few moments later he set the pail down beside his partner and told him what he had decided. Jim Gillis didn't believe him. He poured the water slowly over the pan of dirt he had just dug from the hillside and looked hopefully for nuggets of gold.

"None in this pan," he said at last, turning to Sam. "But in the next one maybe—" He stopped, for he saw that his partner wasn't listening. Sam was seated on a rock, scribbling on a writing pad.

"What are you doing?" Jim Gillis asked.

"Writing a story about a jumping frog," Sam Clemens said. "I heard a fellow talking about a frog race they held over in Calaveras County. And I got to wondering what a bullfrog, like the one my uncle John Quarles had, could do in a race like that. Uncle John used to feed the critter a mixed diet of flies and buckshot and—"

Sam didn't finish the sentence, but he did

[142]

finish his story and signed the name "Mark Twain" to it. He took it to the nearest post office and mailed it to a magazine in the east. Then he went back to San Francisco to do newspaper work again. A week after he left Angel's Camp another man found gold nuggets worth thousands of dollars, right where Sam and Jim Gillis had been mining. But it didn't matter to Sam.

His story about the *Celebrated Jumping Frog of Calaveras County* was published in the eastern magazine. It was so funny that it was printed in many newspapers, too. In a very short time Mark Twain became famous as a writer of humorous stories. Editors all over the country wanted him to write other stories. And the publisher of a California newspaper wanted to send him to the Sandwich Islands, which are now called the Hawaiian Islands.

"Folks in this country know almost nothing about those islands," the editor told Mark Twain. "I want you to write about them and send what you write back to my newspaper. It isn't all to be funny stuff like the *Jumping Frog,* either. We want you to get facts as well as good stories."

Sam was delighted with this assignment. On a fine day in March he sailed for the Sandwich Islands on the steamer *Ajax*. She was a big new steamship, but like all ocean-going steamers of her day, she carried sail. Sam Clemens had never seen anything like her. He explored her from bow to stern.

"Come down from there, sir!" the captain shouted when he spotted Sam climbing like a monkey in the rigging.

"I just wanted a seagull's-eye view," Sam said, jumping down on the deck. "I was trying to figure out how you work all those sails."

"Well, I can't let my passengers climb around in dangerous places," the captain argued. "You're a pretty famous young man, Mr. Twain, but I thought you'd be more interested in frogs than ships."

Sam forgot all about Mark Twain, the newspaperman, on the voyage to the islands. But once the *Ajax* dropped anchor in the sunlit harbor of Honolulu, it was Mark Twain, the reporter, who went to work again.

For two months he visited all the islands. He wrote about the natives and the tropical scenery and the sugar plantations. One whole night he sat staring down into the fiery crater of Kilauea volcano so he could describe it for readers back home. Day after day he rode about the country, taking so little rest that he wore himself out. When he got back to the

hotel in Honolulu, a doctor ordered him to go to bed and stay there.

Two United States Ambassadors had just arrived in Honolulu on their way to China and Japan. When they heard that the author of *The Jumping Frog* was ill they went to the hotel to see him. Mark Twain was honored by their visit, but he was also feeling rather glum.

"Wouldn't you think," he drawled, "that at my age, I could get sick with something more dignified?"

"What *is* wrong with you?" asked one of his distinguished visitors.

"Saddle sores!" Mark Twain said grimly, wincing with pain as he turned over in his bed. "And they're no joke!"

His visitors soon left him. But that same afternoon Edward Burlingame, the eighteen-year-old son of the Ambassador to China, burst into his room.

"Exciting news, Mr. Twain!" he exclaimed. "A ship called the *Hornet* burned at sea forty-three days ago. Fifteen people escaped in an open boat with only ten days' rations. They've managed to keep alive on the ocean all this time. Now they've landed on one of the islands and they're being brought to the hospital here in Honolulu. It would make a wonderful story for your newspaper."

"The biggest story in years!" Mark Twain said. "There's even a ship sailing for San Francisco tomorrow that could take it. And I *would* have saddle sores!"

Slowly and painfully he got out of bed, but he could not walk at all. With a groan, he sank back on his pillows. Soon after Edward left, however, Mark Twain's bedroom door was opened again. In walked the United States Ambassadors with some friends and an army cot.

"Mr. Twain," said Mr. Burlingame, "we have come to take you to the hospital so that you can interview the survivors of the *Hornet*. It's a peculiar way for a reporter to get facts for a story, but—" He interrupted himself to help one of the other men lift Mark Twain to the army cot.

"Now this," Mark Twain drawled as he was carried through Honolulu streets, "is how I'd like to do all my reporting."

At the hospital, Mark Twain was taken from bed to bed, so that he could talk to all the *Hornet* survivors. He spent the night writing the story of the terrible fire and the dreadful weeks in an open lifeboat. In the morning, young Edward got the story aboard the ship just as she was about to sail away.

Mark Twain returned to California several weeks later to find that his dispatches had been read in newspapers from coast to coast. People everywhere wanted to see him and hear more about his experiences on the Sandwich Islands.

"A lecture tour is the way to satisfy them," his editor said.

"Now that's plumb foolish," the author drawled. "I'm no public speaker."

But the public did not agree. Mark Twain was one public speaker whom folks would go any distance to hear. At first he simply could not believe it. Before he gave a lecture his heart would thump and his hands would grow damp. He worried about whether anyone

[148]

would show up to listen to him. Then he was scared because so many people came. He was sure he could never hold their interest.

"Ladies and gentlemen," he always began his talk, "tonight I aim to tell you a little bit about our fellow savages in the Sandwich Islands . . ."

Even when the lecture was over, his audiences wanted to hear more. "Give us the Jumping Frog story!" they would shout. "Tell us your story about the Golden Arm!"

In mining camps and cities and farm towns all across the United States, Mark Twain lectured and told stories.

"It isn't often you listen to somebody that can make you laugh the way Mark Twain can," folks would say to each other, as they left the lecture halls. "A good laugh like that is worth a lot of money."

"He makes you think, too," others said. "Unless you hear him tell it, you can't believe the savages in those far places are folks pretty much like you and me."

In spite of his success, Mark Twain was glad when his lecture tour was over and he could take another newspaper assignment. This time he was to travel to Europe and the countries of the Near East with some people who were going just to see the sights. He was to write about the trip and send his letters to be printed in a California newspaper and a newspaper in New York.

In June, Mark Twain and the party of sightseers set sail from New York on the side-wheel steamship *Quaker City*. The long voyage across the ocean was pleasant, and so was the trip through Europe and the Holy Lands.

Wherever he went, Mark Twain kept his eyes open, listened, and asked questions. When other travelers were resting, he wrote the letters he had promised to send back to America. He hoped to put them all into a book some day, which he would call *Innocents Abroad*.

People in the United States read Mark Twain's letters and many of them nodded their heads knowingly.

"That young man is more than a newspaper reporter," they said. "He is a very great writer."

But Mark Twain had more on his mind than writing when he returned to America. On shipboard he had seen a picture of a lovely young lady who was the sister of one of his friends.

"What's her name?" he had asked his friend.

"Olivia," Charles Langdon had replied. "We call her Livy and she's a wonderful girl."

"I can see that," Mark Twain had said, serious for once.

Since then he had thought a great deal about Olivia Langdon. When he met her, he decided at once that he wanted to marry her.

As for Livy, she found Mark Twain different from anyone she had ever known. He seemed like a bright comet in her quiet world.

On a wintry day two years later, they were married in the Langdons' home in Elmira, New York. Then they took a train for Buffalo, where they planned to live. A number of relatives and friends went with them.

When they reached Buffalo that night, sleighs were waiting at the station. Sam Clemens helped his bride into one of them, tucked a fur robe around her, and climbed in beside her. Soon all the sleighs were filled, and off they started with bells jingling merrily.

Up one street and down another they went. Somehow the sleigh in which Sam and Livy were riding dropped far behind the others. But Sam didn't even notice it. He was worrying because he had not saved up enough money to buy Livy a fine home like the one she had just left. Maybe she wouldn't like the furnished rooms he had rented.

"We won't have to live in a boarding house forever, Livy," he said at last. "Some day I'll buy you a beautiful—"

He stopped speaking as the driver pulled up his horses before a beautiful house blazing with light. In the open doorway stood his sister Pamela, who had come east for his wedding.

"Welcome home!" she called.

Sam was bewildered. "There must be some mistake," he said when he handed Livy out of the sleigh. Still dazed, he tried to answer the warm greetings of Livy's relatives and friends.

At last Livy put her hand on his arm. "Sam, don't you understand?" she asked. "This is *our* house. It's our wedding present from Father."

Sam gulped. Then his eyes twinkled. He turned to his father-in-law, who was standing beside Pamela.

"Mr. Langdon," he said solemnly, "whenever you come to Buffalo after this—even if it's twice a year—you come right here. Stay here overnight if you want to. It won't cost you a cent."

Mr. Langdon laughed. He told the other guests he thought it a very good joke to be invited to stay in the house he himself had just bought.

CHAPTER FIFTEEN

Mark Twain Writes About Tom Sawyer

SAMUEL CLEMENS sat in his hilltop study at Quarry Farm, near Elmira, New York. Livy had spent summers here ever since she was little. This year she and Sam had brought their tiny daughter Susy, and Clara, the new baby, with them.

The study was a summerhouse, eight-sided and built very much like a riverboat pilot house to make Sam feel at home. The fireplace took up one wall. There were big windows in all the other walls so Sam could look out over the whole countryside while he worked.

Usually Sam Clemens turned into Mark Twain the moment he sat down at his worktable. But today, although he was beginning a new book, he stayed very much Sam Clemens.

"Anybody reading the story I am going to write now," he told himself, "will think Mark Twain wrote it. But it'll be Sam's story all the way. *Sam and His Friends*. No, that won't do. I'll give it a new title."

He scratched his ear with his pen handle. Then he wrote on a fresh sheet of paper: *The Adventures of Tom Sawyer*.

He planned that this story would be about a band of boys ranging over hills and fields. Boys who could run like wild turkeys and swim like ducks. No orchard or melon patch was safe from them. And they could *not* stay out of trouble.

The author chuckled as he wrote. Sometimes he talked to himself. He was having a real name-changing party.

The town of Hannibal became St. Petersburg. Holliday's Hill was changed to Cardiff Hill. When he went to work on his characters, John Briggs was called Joe Harper. Sam's sister, Pamela, became Cousin Mary. And Tom Sawyer himself was practically a cross between Sam Clemens and Will Bowen.

"I reckon we're a fair-sized rascal between us," Sam said, half aloud. "Now Tom Blankenship—I gave him a new name back in the old days. *Finn,* it was. Huckleberry will go with Finn. Tom was always powerful partial to huckleberries."

Sam Clemens went on remembering bits of his past to put into the new story. There was the day he tricked the boys into whitewashing a fence. And the time he gave one of the cats a dose of Pain Killer. Maybe he could get in a creepy scene in the cave. The cave reminded him of Laura Hawkins, so he put her into the story and changed her name to Becky Thatcher.

In spite of seven windows, the room was growing dark when the author gathered up scattered sheets of paper from table and floor. He wanted to read them to Livy after supper down at the farmhouse. Walking down the hill, he wondered how their new house in Hartford, Connecticut, was getting along. At last he was building for his Livy a house as big as his dreams.

Livy thought her husband's new book was his best. And she loved her big new home when they moved into it.

The years passed quickly for the Clemens

family. When a third little girl was born, they were all delighted. Though Mark Twain was very busy, he always found time to play with Susy, Clara, and tiny Jean.

One day he went to Susy's room to look for her. She was not there, but on her bed was a black copybook filled with her large round handwriting. Mark Twain opened it and read a few lines. Then he smiled. Susy had been writing about him!

"We are a very happy family!" Susy had begun. "We consist of Papa, Mama, Jean, Clara, and me. It is Papa I am writing about, and I shall have no trouble in not knowing what to say about him, as he is a very striking character.

"Papa is a very good man, and a very funny one. He *has* got a temper, but we all of us have in this family. And he is, oh, so absent-minded. He blows soap bubbles for us filled with tobacco smoke. There are eleven cats at the farm here now and our donkey Kiditchin. Papa's favorite is a little tortoise-shell kitten he has named Sour Mash.

"Our various occupations are as follows: Papa rises about ½ past 7, writes, and plays tennis with Clara and me, and tries to make the donkey go in the morning. He started to

ride Kiditchin to show us how, but Kiditchin threw him over her head. Papa thinks she didn't like the poem he wrote about her; it is mostly her own song that goes 'Waw—he!' ''

Mark Twain chuckled when he read that. "Why, the young rascal," he said, "how well she knows me!"

Susy went on to tell about the Hartford house with all its little balconies and the mantelpiece brought from a ruined castle in Scotland. She said they needed a big house because they had to entertain famous people and because kinfolk so often stayed with them. Susy's two grandmothers were there, and her aunt Pamela and uncle Orion and all their families.

She wrote next about the billiard room with the big green table, where Papa played with other famous gentlemen. When he didn't have visitors, he played billiards with the cats. Sour Mash, Sin and Satan, Stray Kit and Fanny and Motley all loved to sit in the pockets of the billiard table and snatch at the balls he rolled to them.

"Papa has done a great deal in his life I think that is good and very remarkable," Susy wrote. "He is known to the public as a humorist, but he has much more in him that is earnest than that is humorous."

Susy's mother had told her of many kind deeds her father never talked about. One of these was sending a colored man through Yale University. That was partly in memory of a little Negro boy named Sandy and because Mark Twain said every white man owed a debt to every colored man.

Susy and her mother, Mark Twain read much later on in Susy's copybook, were very much troubled since he had gone into partnership with his cousin Charles Webster in a publishing business. He had published General Grant's books, but he seemed to be forgetting his own work. One evening, Susy had written, her father told her he didn't expect to write but one more book. It was to be about a Connecticut Yankee who went to the court of King Arthur.

Mark Twain was very glad his daughter Susy didn't want him to stop writing books. And Susy need not have worried, because he never really did stop all his life long.

CHAPTER SIXTEEN

The Conquering Hero Comes Home

"MARK TWAIN!" The leadsman calling the sounding looked up at the old man in the white suit standing on the hurricane deck.

It was the famous author who had taken his pen name from that call, "Mark twain!" He was staring down, watching the wake the paddlewheel cut through the water. He could hardly believe that so many years had passed since he last looked at the Mississippi.

Mark Twain had written a great many books. He was known all over the world and he had dined with kings and presidents. But none of his fame seemed as real to him as this old river.

"Sam! Sam Clemens! You remember me?" As the steamboat docked at Hannibal, an old

"What's the town all decorated up for?"

man broke through the crowd calling to the visitor coming down the gangplank.

"Of course I remember you, John Briggs." Mark Twain looked up the street from the levee. "What's the town all decorated up for? Have you changed the date of the Fourth of July in Missouri?"

"The trimmings are for you, Sam. You're supposed to be the conquering hero today. How does it make you feel?"

"Mighty small, John." Sam's drawl was as long as ever. "Just about ten-year size."

"I heard you've been gadding round the world on a speaking trip again," John said. "Why'd you want to do that at your age?"

"I didn't want to, John. I had to do it. My publishing firm failed and I was in debt. And all the way round the globe, folks paid good money to look at the biggest danged fool in the world. I just threw in my talks free."

"Did you find anything new in those foreign parts?" John Briggs asked. He himself had never gone away from Hannibal.

"Reckon so, John. I learned that people laugh at the same things all over the world. A gentleman in India wearing a turban could repeat the Jumping Frog story word for word. And in Australia they ate up that one about the Golden Arm. It's a small world, as some fellow said."

Sam did not tell his old friend that Susy had died while he was away from home. He was always ready to share laughs with other people, but his sorrows he kept to himself.

It might be a small world, but it was a very small house that photographers asked Mark Twain to pose in front of. He had to look twice before he recognized his old home.

"It's shrunk!" he told John. "A boy's home is a big place to him. If I'd waited another ten years to come back, most likely this wouldn't look any bigger than a birdcage."

All Hannibal made a fuss over Mark Twain, with dinners and speeches. Everybody wanted to shake his hand. He even found himself making a speech at the Sunday School.

"When I was a little boy in Hannibal," he told the children in his slow, solemn voice, "I used to play hereabouts with my friends. I don't suppose there are any little boys here as good as we were. It's not to be expected. Little boys in those days were always good little boys,

[165]

because those were the good old days when everything was better than it is now."

Grandchildren and great-grandchildren of his old friends wriggled with delight as they listened to this old man with the curly white hair and twinkly eyes. They had all read *Tom Sawyer,* so they knew a lot about those good old days. The grown folks sitting on the back benches were laughing a lot, too.

"You still think you're *some,* don't you, Sam Clemens?" an ancient voice cackled when Sam went down the steps afterwards. Jimmy McDaniel, now a wrinkled old man, held out a hand like a claw.

On Sunday afternoon, Sam and John went up to Holliday's Hill.

"There's no lovelier sight in the whole world than this," Sam said. "I can see where we used to swim and the orchard where we stole peaches. And a rock across the road. That's a big rock."

About three thousand Sundays had gone by since they sent that rock flying down the hill. But both Sam and John felt a shiver when they looked at it.

"The town is aiming to blast it out of

there," John said. "With building going on out this way, it's a nuisance."

They talked about old friends. Will Bowen had worked on the river after he came back from the war, and he died on the river. Sam's brother Henry had died in a steamboat accident on the river, too. Tom Blankenship had gone west and become the sheriff of a town in Montana.

"It seems funny to think we're old men," Mark Twain drawled. "And here's the hill still as green as it was all those years ago. I reckon this is the last time we'll meet, John."

"Don't be in a rush to say good-by," John

Briggs told him. "I'm going along to St. Louis tomorrow to watch that steamboat christening you're attending there."

"What's special about it?" Sam asked. "I don't even know why they made a point of me being there."

The next day, in St. Louis, the Governor of Missouri made a long speech about their distinguished visitor, Mr. Mark Twain. A French countess whose ancestor was the first white man to explore the Mississippi River stood holding a champagne bottle, ready to christen the new river steamer.

At last the moment arrived. Workmen knocked away the wooden planks that were holding the ship in the ways. As she slid down into the water, the bottle cracked smartly and champagne bubbled over her shiny paintwork.

"I christen thee, good ship, MARK TWAIN!" the lady cried.

Somewhere behind him, Sam Clemens could hear John Briggs laughing. It was because the ship was being named for his best friend that John had been so anxious to attend the launching.

CHAPTER SEVENTEEN

Halley's Comet Comes Again

THE great man lay in his bed. His hair was as white as his pillow. Three kittens lay curled up asleep on his feet.

It was a golden spring day. The curtain at Mark Twain's open window blew gently in a breeze that was very warm for April. He could hear Clara down below talking to the gardener.

"As soon as the crocuses and daffodils are finished, we'll have blue iris coming along," Clara said.

Clara was the only one of Mark Twain's children still alive. His Livy had died, too, after all the years she had been so close to him. Mark Twain was left to the company of his memories. On the whole, they were very good memories.

He did wish that Livy and Susy had lived to go to England with him on his last trip which he had made three years ago. That was when the great University of Oxford had given him the highest honor they could by making him a "Doctor of Letters."

Doctor of Letters is a degree that scholars can earn only after many years of study in a college. But Sam had earned it by the wonderful books he had written, for they made him more truly a Doctor of Letters than any amount of study could do.

Mark Twain had been very proud when he stood on the platform in a scarlet and black gown. The Oxford students had cheered him again and again. So the chancellor of the University had to wait for a long time until his voice could be heard.

"Most amiable and charming sir," the chancellor had said at last to Mark Twain, "you shake the sides of the whole world with your merriment. We rejoice to honor you here."

Then the chancellor had made a long speech, telling how Mark Twain had made the world a better place with his humor and truth. The old man chuckled as he lay in his bed, remembering it. Miss Mary Ann Newcomb should have been there with him! How surprised she would have been to see her champion hookey player in such company! And to hear such words spoken about him.

Mark Twain had received a great many other honors in his long life, but he wasn't thinking about them now. He was trying to name over the books he had written, but there were so many that he could not name them all. He could remember telling folks about river steamboating in *Life on the Mississippi,* and about the old West and mining camps in a book called *Roughing It.*

Then there were the books that children the world over would never let him forget. He often received letters from boys and girls about *Tom Sawyer* and *Huckleberry Finn,* about *The Prince and the Pauper* and *A Connecticut Yankee in King Arthur's Court.*

One of the last books he had written had been a life of St. Joan of Arc. Thinking about it always reminded him of the day he found a torn page on the street in Hannibal. That was the day he discovered how wonderful books really are.

"Oh, Edward," Clara's voice reached Mark Twain again as she spoke to the gardener, "don't forget to watch the sky tonight. The newspaper says we'll be able to see Halley's Comet. It is seventy-five years since it appeared last."

"Well, think of that, ma'am!" the gardener exclaimed.

Mark Twain thought about it, too. It took him back to another spring day when Sam Clemens played hookey with some of his

friends in a hideout on Bear Creek. That was
the day Sam Clemens began giving himself
some fine new names. Names like Captain
Blankenship of the *Big Missouri*. Names like
Mark Twain.

It was the day the fish that got away was a
big comet with a goldy yellow tail, to hear
little Sam tell it. A Halley's Comet.

"I told Will and Tom and the others about
that," Mark Twain murmured. He began to
chuckle and one of the kittens purred in its
sleep. "I said I came in with Halley's Comet
and I meant to stay till Halley's Comet came
back again. I made it, too."

He was an old, old man lying in his bed.

[*173*]

But at that moment, his voice wasn't old at all. It was just young Sam Clemens' "long talk."

It was the "long talk" that had charmed the world and made Mark Twain more friends than he could count.

About the Author

JOAN HOWARD was born in British Columbia. Her childhood was spent in places as far apart as England and Alaska and India. Wherever the family moved, she took her beloved bull terrier and many cats. Pets were outnumbered only by books, and Joan Howard learned more from reading than from school, though she did go to college later. She began to write stories when she was very young and has written several books for boys and girls. She lives now on the very edge of the Atlantic Ocean, with high tide in the front yard, and her family of husband and son is enlarged by one dog, a lot of cats, and many visiting sea gulls.

About the Artist

DONALD McKAY was born in San Francisco, California. When he was twelve, he spent a year with his grandfather, who taught school in the Hawaiian Islands. Although his grandfather was eighty years old, he liked fast horses and would drive like the wind in a two-wheeled cart with young Donald by his side. They had many accidents, but Donald McKay still recalls those wild rides as his most exciting experiences. When he returned to the U. S., he attended the California School of Fine Arts and later the Art Students League. After a year in World War I, he began to illustrate the Mark Twain classics that made him famous. He is married and has one young daughter—a redhead.

★ 1 *Born in Florida, Mo., November 30, 1835*

★ 2 *Starts his apprenticeship t a printer, 1848*

★ 3 *Receives his license as a Mississippi River pilot, 1858*

★ 4 *First uses the name of Mark Twain, 1863*

★ 10 *Dies at Redding, Conn., April 21, 1910*

★ 9 *Receives degree of Doctor of Letter Oxford University, England, 1*